WHY IS HE STILL HERE?

By Max Toper

To my wonderful Baba
You were the best grandfather anyone could
ask for. In these pages and in my heart, you
will live on.

DISCLAIMER

This book is a memoir, reflecting the author's recollections of the life experiences he has had to date. To safeguard identities, the names and characteristics of places and persons have been changed. For this same purpose, some events have also been altered. The author does not intend to defame individuals nor cause personal or professional harm.

Chapter 1: Early Years

Childish laughter, diverse colourful toys. It is an infant's meadow, a "playgroup". Aged three years old, I carefully observe my peers. One child glances at me. I'm sealed in stasis, armpits burning. Only discharged from bondage when he strikes an interest in Play-Doh. Back to the train track – my train track. Hands trembling, soaked in sweat, the last piece of track added. I finish my masterpiece.

'Max, do you want to play with the Play-Doh?' mum suggests, biting her lip.

I marvel at my work. It encompasses all sides of the room, snaking under tables, all connecting up with impeccable order. It never once drifts into the middle. That is where the other toddlers play.

'Okay,' I mumble, staggering to my feet, head bowed, stumbling over to the table before joining mum. Arm muscles becoming faint, icy, I concentrate on the Play-Doh. Only mum and I exist; the others do not. They cannot.

Laughter, babbling, the whoosh of a train set unravelling. The girl rips through my achievement. Pieces that were previously planted in order now altered into shattered fragments. She glances up at me. With inborn, primordial reflex, my gaze scampers out of the way.

'Max?' Mum calls. 'What's wrong?' The pure laughter of the infants vanishes, disappearing into the deathly shrieks of one girl. My nails are talons, ravaging her hair, her flesh. A once joyous face stuck in a predator's grasp. She has prodded the hornet's nest.

Mum rushes over, facing the scorn of other parents and trying to ignore the orchestra of tears erupting from their offspring. There is no aid from anyone as she attempts to free the meek prey. The beast is defiant, teeth gritted, claws slashing. Ultimately, through pure grit, mum yanks him from the playgroup, this time for good. He won't any longer be able to harm the other children.

That beast is a boy. That boy is me. When I started writing this book, I was sixteen years old. At age five, I was diagnosed with autism spectrum disorder and ADHD, among other things. But such labels aren't my identity. I am my identity and this is my story. I'm not here to claim "victimhood" at the hands of an "ableist society", nor to "dismantle stereotypes". I write because I enjoy storytelling. I don't know what I'd do without film and literature. So why not make my own contribution to humanity's grand collection? My story, whose main motivation is to explain "why I'm still here". This book isn't magic, I don't have all the answers. I'm just someone with a computer that glows purple, which is snazzy, if I say so myself.

I grew up in the suburbs of London and owned a teddy bear named William. I loved music and baking with my grandmother. I watched Postman Pat, had tons of LEGO and adored computers. Most would have considered me your average toddler, but fate isn't kind to all. There were enormous disparities between me and the average child in Britain, most of them physical.

Mum's attempts at breastfeeding me lasted mere days. I couldn't do it, the muscles around my mouth being too lax to suckle. Without nutrients, I failed to put on any weight, and missed out on a crucial stage of early development. Even after switching to a bottle, I always remained dangerously underweight. Beyond that, I put nothing in my mouth as a baby, no doubt to spare my parents the worry.

I crawled late, at 11 months. I also walked late, at 21 months. My first tooth appeared late, at 13 months. It was easy to knock me off my feet; I stumbled regularly. I seldom made eye contact. In fact, my vision was nowhere near the standards of my peers. But nobody realised and, being a toddler, I didn't notice such things.

People called my speech articulate, but only grandma realised that because of my weak oral muscles, I couldn't pronounce the letter *F* correctly. I had a bottle going to bed until the age of ten and wet the bed until the age of eleven.

I played with my parents' hair for comfort until I grew into a teenager. Toilet training is another story. Imagine yourself at five years old. You're on a playground with lots of other children. You pause: is a boulder wedged in your buttocks? The brain slows to a slither, muscles go on holiday. Life is wrung from your body. You're certainly not running to the toilet. Excrement rolls down your trousers and onto the concrete. At least it wasn't runny this time. A tiny rock of solid faeces. Everyone is staring at you. A teacher sighs, plodding toward you. You've had another 'incident'. But that wasn't you, it was me. Not toilet-trained until I was ten, just in time for secondary school. Oh, did I mention I'm an August child? Youngest in my year.

Mum gave up on toilet training. For a while I was condemned to nappies at school, praying nobody would notice. Albeit, if you saw past these and other developmental issues, I was ordinary.

Still there were things about my condition that took everyone a long time to understand, including me. As a toddler I cherished the swings, causing long queues in the playground. The thrilling sensation of going up in the air and back down was desperately needed because, at times, I must release "energy". Over the years I developed techniques, like jumping up and down in private or rocking on the floor. But back then the exhilaration of a swing or lying down and kicking my legs up in the air proved the only remedies that

4

worked. I don't know why I need this physical stimulation. It's not something I want to argue with, or even could argue with, as my body often betrays me.

Violence. That playgroup wasn't an isolated incident. Another child wanders too close? Whack! So mum and dad tried "consequences". But though I hated losing my toys, or sitting in "time out", my behaviour was impossible to change, even with a conscious effort. Sometimes, it was a reflex. At other times, an unfortunate peer would brush against me or push in on the slide. I couldn't contain my tidal wave of a temper.

This didn't make me a candidate for a civilised nursery. The first one I went to was in a converted house near my grandparents' flat. I remember little about it except that the teacher ruled with an iron fist. Children shivered when she called their names. Usually she'd glare at me and my grandfather when he collected me.

I defecated in the playground, hit a few children. The placement lasted for all of three weeks. Mum and dad were constantly working, earning money to move us out of our tiny flat. They could not home-school me, and a decision had to be made about my education. My family is not religious, and I enjoy a bacon roll. Yet everyone felt I would be happier in a Jewish school. Off I travelled to Blue House Primary. The school was very new at the time I first went there. The classrooms were spotless, with fresh pencils and frequently painted walls. The nursery playground had quaint playhouses. Somehow, despite my behaviour being troublesome we'd arrive on time every morning. The enormous building towered over me.

To get to class, we would trudge through a minefield of older children. I'd regularly crash face first into the concrete. Classmates loved walking along the small brick walls; maybe they were practising for the tightrope. I tried it myself, but never made it unless my parents or grandparents helped me. *Why can they do it?* Whoever was dropping me off would leave me in the playground. Most kids cried, but I was too busy inspecting every movement they made. Screams, giggles, crying. I would struggle to discern if any of these noises were hostile.

With sixty kids in one playground. I'd get knocked over and they'd get a thrashing. Mum got a call and had a few angry confrontations. But kids are intelligent, and I was the smallest in my class. Soon they realised I couldn't climb, so tormenting me became a game. Say something unkind to Max, or invade his personal space. He will chase you. Run and laugh, then escape to the climbing frame, where he could never hope to reach you – for he is too weak.

Jewish schools have a dress code: *kippa, tzitzits* and an itchy woollen uniform. Underneath that is a shirt, which has a label cutting at your neck, trying to sever your head. To stay matted to your hair, the *kippa* requires a clip. It might as well have been a computer chip embedded to my skull. The noise it made when I walked was a never-ending ding. If I took it off, teachers would wrestle me to the floor, welding it back on my head. As for *tzitzits* mummy put my clothes on me in the morning. Imagine undoing those in the toilet, even if you make it there before defecating. Like steel chains, they stubbornly refuse to release you.

The nursery had two classes. Mrs. Lionel, my teacher, often praised my reading skills and excused some of the more "uncultured" etiquette I displayed. Mrs. Posner ran the other class and was usually the one to reprimand me if I broke the school rules to even the smallest degree.

Back to my peers, every time they mocked me, I sought revenge. When they least expected it, I'd rip off their *kippas* and flush them down the toilet. After they were miraculously retrieved from the sewers, mum ended up having to wash them all. Other times I'd take the direct approach, clawing their faces and ripping out large clumps of their hair. Classmates seldom expected it. I was fun to torment on the playground but a nightmare at seemingly random moments. Whereas they soon forgot about me, I would remember. Watching as they outclassed me in every area: handwriting, athleticism, friends.

Revenge was something I enjoyed; I was good at it. The other children let things go; I didn't. It was the only way to exert my will, to protect myself. I remember developing a "bad guy" persona and mentality. Like the ones you see on children's cartoons, they only exist to cause trouble, nothing more. I saw the world in a similarly cartoonish light. The bad-guy me would do something "evil". The "good" teachers were superheroes, locking me away where I belonged. I couldn't see anything beyond that role; perhaps I was born to play it. Nothing else worked, and it did give me a sense of power. A fleeting yet cherished ecstasy.

Call my infant-self a hypocrite, but I also wanted to be friends with the other children. To put it bluntly, I craved what they had, yet voluntarily played the role of villain, this being the only one that made sense of who I thought I was. I was barred from most of the class' birthday parties. Mum didn't want me left out, so she hosted birthday parties for me. In response, a parent came up to me and mum with their child in tow, ripping up the invitation in front of us.

The child was crying and screaming. 'I don't want to go,' he wailed, and kept repeating those words. I blinked repeatedly, struggling to repress the tears.

Surprisingly, I ended up making a friend that year, a boy called Bradley. Both of us enjoyed wooden train tracks, I suppose. Why did I trust him over the others? I don't remember exactly, but maybe because he trusted me. At one point in the school year, Mrs. Lionel took my parents aside.

'Something is very wrong,' she told them. One thing led to another and suddenly I was in a paediatrician's office. Hypotonia, my first diagnosis. It meant nothing to me, as medical terms were beyond my understanding at such a young age.

Soon I was off to reception. But unlike the other children, the teachers forced me to sit on a spiky blue cushion. At night I'd discover the spikes had pressed splotchy marks into my flesh. That and the searing pain I experienced every time I sat on one of these cushions were why I always threw them out of the classroom every time I saw one.

So, reception, but where do I begin? One kid battered me in an unprovoked attack, and I got blamed for it by one teacher. Sports day was a disaster, I lost every game. The teacher refused to have my drawings on the wall. And by reception my paediatrician had reached a diagnosis of "severe dyspraxia", and I was also the only child in my class wearing glasses. Not standard glasses, though, but prism glasses to prevent what my dad told me was 'terrible eyesight that will be dangerous when you're older'.

Perhaps it was the fear behind his words that swayed me, but wearing them made me feel special, so I never refused. Coming back to my social circle, I was thrown out of class party after class party. And a spree of brawls in a soft-play centre saw another parent threaten to beat dad into hospital.

Most experts who came to assess me dismissed everything as "behavioural", i.e., the fault of my parents. I sat at the back of the class, having only one friend who played with me and even then less and less so. It seemed I was indeed the "bad guy", yet I couldn't understand why. Did the world just hate me? Nobody else behaved as I did – as my body did.

Inexplicably, I was not expelled. I'd scraped through the toddler years, and my small world now began to expand. Dad accumulated the funds to move us into a house, and in September that year I would move up to year one. Finally, I was in primary school, a "big boy" at last.

Chapter 2: The Rainbow Room

Our new house, boxes everywhere. Naturally, I chose the biggest bedroom and started to make myself comfortable, but bare walls and wide unfurnished spaces are tough to call home. It was unfamiliar, just like my new classroom, which, though furnished, had a starkly modern touch. Perfectly arranged desks, children assembling in front of a smart board. The entire school resembled a stock photo.

Mrs. Gideon, our teacher, had little patience for my "antics". The ring of her words resounded in my ears long after they left her mouth, giving way to bitter tears and a body set aflame.

'Don't do that,' she bellowed. 'I'm not playing games, Max. I will tell your parents about this.'

If I attacked her, I'd be restrained in milliseconds. If I ran out of class, Mrs. Gideon's assistant, Mrs. Hickman, would drag me back. Personally, I can't recall a day we weren't at odds.

Most of the lessons took place on a carpet in front of the smart board. I'd sit on that accursed spiky blue cushion. At first, they permitted me to sit near my peers. Within a week, they had squashed me into a corner with a tiny desk. I tried to take part in the lessons. If Mrs. Gideon was reading something to the class, I'd move my chair as close as they allowed. Head tilted, I'd listen.

Beyond that, unless it was computing, I'd struggle to participate. When assigned a handwriting task, the classroom's paper supply vanished. For reasons I don't remember, Mrs. Gideon wouldn't allow me to use an eraser, so if I made a mistake I'd need a fresh sheet. What was the point in participating? The teachers only seemed to provide fleeting acknowledgment and praise. Therefore, I sat isolated, reading whatever books I found.

As I took part less and less in classroom activities, I began doing my own. I read books, made rudimentary arts and crafts, and taught myself how to use scissors. My peers found these things and others straightforward, so I thought learning to do them would bring me closer to acceptance in school. But I'd soon discover that unlike my peers, I had to be inventive, and find strategies when my body refused to cooperate. Often, raw determination saw me through. Every achievement represented something I thought I'd never be able to do. My cheeks turned red with pride. I'd have to jump up and down, behaviour which Mrs. Gideon responded to with shouting and scornful glares.

One day I took a pair of scissors and made a "chick". As I recall, it was a sheet of paper cut into what I thought looked like a baby chicken. This is the sole creation I remember, because it was the first time I had used a pair of scissors successfully. At break-time I showed it to Bradley, only for another boy to knock me to the ground. I reached out to hit him, only to have my hand trampled on. Mouth dry, I squinted at my assailant, the same boy who had beaten me to the floor the previous year. Visions of that day still tormented me. I couldn't let him press the advantage, so I attempted to bite his leg. He yelped back, but my attack was a ploy, something to distract him as I staggered to my feet. We faced each other. Bradley's lip muscles moved, albeit no words escaped his mouth.

'Mrs. Gideon,' I called. No response, as she continued talking to Mrs. Hickman. 'Mrs. Gideon?' Nope, no help is coming.

The boy smirked, snatching at my creation and tearing it to shreds. Inflamed tears welled up in my eyes. Bradley backed away. The enemy was bigger, but I had no choice. Run and he would catch me; do nothing and he'd beat me senseless; fight and I might win. Charging into the face of doom, I bit my tormentor's arm. A fist slammed into my chest. Breath trembling, I caught myself.

'Mrs. Gideon,' my assailant called with a sickening grin.

She sprinted over with Mrs. Hickman. They forced me to the floor, detaining me as I hollered. Nobody listened, Bradley did nothing. I was left alone in the classroom to cry whilst they soothed the boy I viewed as the undeniable aggressor.

In another incident, I defecated in class. Out of shame, I hid the small pellet in my desk. The school cleaners found it. The school telephoned my parents. Mrs. Gideon took me before the class. She told my peers, smiling as she lectured on the 'importance of hygiene'. Some giggled, others stared blankly, their jaws hanging open.

***

'Dad, I want to be a normal boy,' I said as we were driving home from school, "No Cars Go" by Arcade Fire playing in the background. Either dad played that or "A Jigsaw Falling into Place" by Radiohead.

'You're normal to us. We love you,' dad said to console me.

'Nobody else does.'

'Nonsense, grandma and baba love you.'

Face squeezed against the window, taking in the music, I wondered why it seemed that the rest of the world hated me. Sadly, things would continue to spiral downward. A new boy called Benjamin Goldstein joined our class. He got friendly with Bradley. I didn't mind this. People had often encouraged me to "share", so perhaps this was my chance. I'd try to join in, and Benjamin would order Bradley away from me. No matter what, he dismissed all requests for us three to play together. My attempts to "share" had failed, and I could only seethe as Benjamin "stole Bradley".

'Why can't you all play together?' adults suggested.

For the most part, I sought to follow through on this advice. It never worked; Benjamin just avoided me. I'd clench my jaw as they played together. An appalling sight. *Get rid of Benjamin and get Bradley back* became the sole focus of my thoughts. I hurled insults, made virulent threats, hurt him. I would beam and Benjamin would break down. Bradley was no longer a focus; the thrilling ecstasy of power its own reward. If I got in trouble, it didn't matter. It was all part of being the "bad guy".

All good villains need their minions, so I used two twins, telling them, 'It's fun, you won't get into trouble'. They didn't, and together we would bully Benjamin, destroying his possessions, taunting him when he cried. Every day, every lesson, every hour, there was no avoiding our wrath. His father threatened to sue my family, and the situation with me in class had reached a breaking point. Therefore, the school decided I should spend lunchtime in the Rainbow Room. My face dropped when there weren't any rainbows. The room was drab, miniature, with a dirty carpet that may as well have been mouldy concrete. With no windows, it was effectively my prison at lunchtime. It was in a compound you had to enter through two enormous doors in the cafeteria. If

I had to guess, the Rainbow Room and other rooms in the school changed purposes often.

There were toys and some computers. They allowed me to play with them if I didn't cause "trouble". It meant they didn't have to worry about me outside of lessons. Soon, various incidents would change that. One involved a ball in the school tuckshop. It was close to the classroom. I'd brought a pound from home to spend.

When I passed there during lunchbreak, my eyes fixated on a small football, the mini kind. I had the money. Mrs. Hickman told me I could buy it later, after school had ended. That lunchtime, the Rainbow Room shook with my jumping. After school, I made my way to the tuckshop. With a smile, I gave a pound to the clerk.

'You can't buy that, Max' called Mrs. Gideon.

How did she know? 'Why, why not?'

She sighed, banging her hands together. 'Chop, chop, home time.'

I fell back. She motioned to the clerk, who threw the ball. Before I could blink, Mrs. Gideon caught it.

'Mrs. Hickman said I could buy it,' I cried, my eyes filling with tears as I attempted to reach for the ball. She forced me aside.

'Mrs. Hickman made a mistake. Come on, your mummy is waiting.' Every word was a sharper needle. 'Max, I don't have time for this nonsense. You will come outside with me.' She grabbed my skinny arm with such force that the bones seemed to wince under the pressure. Legs scraping, dragged outside, I was handed to mum like yesterday's rubbish.

***

Episode two, the fire alarm. The twins I'd enlisted as "minions" identified a glossy red button. I pressed it. The school erupted in the shrill blaring of the fire alarm. It was an honest mistake. I didn't understand what it did. Two teachers grabbed me by the arms, dragging me upstairs, my knees bashing against every step, like a prisoner of war being taken before the warden. In my case, that was the head teacher, who defaulted to a vicious rant at the sight of me.

'He did what?' asked grandpa.

'I pushed a button, baba,' I said.

The head teacher continued her tsunami of rage, arms flapping about at a thousand miles a second. My grandfather winced, barely stifling a laugh.

***

Back at my grandparents' flat, I sat with my head bowed in front of the television, my lower body covered in carpet burns and bruises. My nose was splotchy and withered, as if someone had crushed it with a brick.

I received a letter from the head teacher, addressed to me, which grandma read out.

17

"Do you know how many children we have in school?"

I'd say the fire-alarm incident, coming on top of many others, ended my days in the classroom. School became the Rainbow Room.

When I entered in the morning, two teachers escorted me there and back. The same went for home time. They sealed me in there for hours. Nobody came unless I cried until my throat pleaded for mercy. And the person who regularly came? She was my jailer, a teaching assistant or TA for short. Playing the role of jailer, she never let me out of her sight. Every time I ran out into the complex, she would shout, wrestle me to the floor, and pin me down with bulky objects, and all the while I wept and howled for dear life.

Time on the computers was a rare luxury, and it introduced me to some older children. One boy showed me Miniclip, a site where you played games for free. He had other friends he could have been with. Instead, he and this girl hung out with a five-year-old. Lunchtimes with them were the only times I'd openly smile. I never understood why they showed me such kindness. The concept of older children caring for me like a friend was alien.

When they left, my TA would take over. No learning, no fun. They paid her to leave me to rot in dirty nappies. On one occasion when I bit her jumper in defiance, she tried to pin me to the floor with a giant stuffed platypus.

'He bit my jumper,' she boomed, holding up a sleeve to show the bite marks.

'I can't see them,' dad replied.

'Look closer.'

He raised an eyebrow, 'Can't see a thing. I'm sure your jumper will survive.'

Much screeching followed from the TA. Dad wasn't allowed in the building after that.

Those were my school days from then on at Blue House Primary. Eventually, they withheld permission from the older children to enter the Rainbow Room. The bad guy always goes to jail. They left me to sob. My trousers were always soaking. There was nothing to do but reflect. How had I got here? After all, it was Benjamin who had stolen Bradley. How could they do this? Why would they do this? If they had just paid attention, I wouldn't have been there.

**

A woman visited me. She bought toys, asked me questions and ran through "exercises".

'That's the TARDIS,' I pointed out.

'Oh, what does that do?' The woman asked.

'I ... we can go anywhere.'

She visited weekly until one day I ended up in a room with my parents. It looked like a hospital of some sort, complete with adults claiming to be "doctors". They asked me many questions.

'Why do you hurt Benjamin? He's bigger than you.'

'He's bigger than me, but he's easy to hurt.'

Besides the questions, they asked me to draw pictures. The ones I presented involved me harming children in a variety of ways. I even built a "child killing machine" with the chairs in the reception room. I had reinvented the guillotine. The child's head would catch between the chairs, and "fall off". I was playing my role as the bad guy, and killing is what a real villain does.

'They can't cope with you' mum explained. 'You're going to a new school. We'll visit soon.'

All I recall is being given a card, signed by students and staff. Suddenly I was away, with grandpa, grandma and my teddy bear, William. I never set foot in Blue House Primary again.

Chapter 3: Meadows

A jam sandwich, LEGO, a woman with smoky-grey hair and rich brown eyes. Her smile was scintillating. Outside, relentless rainfall battered the shabby roof. She called this building "Meadows". To my confusion, it turned out to be a long, thin shed painted weatherworn white.

I didn't think of it as a school. The playground was no bigger than our garden. Yet mum and dad had been smiling about it for weeks. Was the school gate a time machine? Had we travelled to another planet? Meadows could have been a pocket universe in itself, because behind the bony walls stood its cousin, White Mountain School.

Blue House Primary represented the pinnacle of modern architecture. White Mountain and Meadows? Relics from the nineteenth century. But this woman, Ciandra. No teacher had ever made me a jam sandwich and organised LEGO to play with. She showed us 'Meadows'. Her voice was breezy, every step serene.

Mosaics adorned an otherwise dull hallway. Children had painted colourful cartoon characters on the toilet doors. Photos of beaming children were everywhere. The school had two classrooms, each with five children. When we entered one of them, the sound of passionate singing greeted us. Adults, children, sat in a circle. All grins, their faces beaming like chandeliers. None of them were singers, but you could swear they wanted the song to last forever. Legs tremored, sweat emerged, my body urged retreat. For the first time, I ignored anxiety's howl. I arrived afraid and left with my perception of "school" shattered.

***

Six years old in August, I arrived in Meadows that September. Some Meadows children got transported there and back in a special bus. I sat away from the other passengers. They were older, bigger, and I was just a tiny thing. The tallest boy, Logan, curled his lip whenever he saw me. Fortunately, I wasn't his focus, at least for now. Instead, he teased a girl called Amelia, beaming as she screamed for him to stop. The escort sighed, discarding her cigarette. She didn't intervene. Therefore, it continued every morning.

Upon arrival my new teacher, Chen, led me inside. They placed me in a class called "Pilots", as the children there were my age group. We'd build hobbyhorses, sing, and play with water and sand. One of our lessons was a trip to a café. They treated us to a meal and taught us how to order food. Unlike Blue House Primary, Meadows didn't prioritise academia. Cultures, religious festivals, friendship. I suppose the Meadows staff wanted us to learn about the world first.

What was the consequence for inappropriate behaviour? If I hit someone, Ciandra restrained me in her office. When I calmed down, she only requested I apologise.

'That's it?' I asked, lightly clasping my throat. 'You're not angry?'

'Tomorrow's a new day,' she replied. That was always her reply. Nobody held anything over my head. I made a friend faster than in Blue House Primary, a boy called Owen.

'I can't climb,' I quavered.

'It's easy. Watch,' he replied. I copied his movements, scaling a climbing frame for the first time in my life. There was a slow, shaky smile on my face when I reached the top. Since that day, we've always been friends. Mum was on the brink of tears when she saw us. The nightmare of Blue House Primary was already a distant memory. Ciandra preferred birthday parties to shouting, hosting one for each child.

I forged fresh memories every day. And "healthy eating"? Tossed out the window, as the staff treated us to all the confectionery items you can think of. If Ciandra didn't have your favourite, she'd buy it. Even one of our rewards for good behaviour was a trip to the corner shop.

Lunchtime was my favourite. Ciandra let me eat at the other computer in her office. She'd microwave my food, and I would enjoy internet access. YouTube, the band Muse, LEGO forums. All revolutionary discoveries for a six-year-old.

***

'Why is he in here?' Logan questioned. My legs twitched, my hand clenched into a fist. Ciandra stood in the doorway, denying him entry. I never understood it, but if he saw another student with Ciandra, his face would scrunch up like an angry pit bull.

'He's having his lunch,' she replied. 'How are you finding mainstream?'

He glanced at the floor, blinking. 'Susan's horrible.'

'I'm sorry, my lovely. Would you like me to—'

'No, forget it.' He jabbed a finger toward me. 'He better not be in here tomorrow.'

***

If I spoke on the bus, Logan would tell me to 'Shut up.'

'Logan is a mango,' I'd chant. He'd grit his teeth and snarl. He was eleven, I was six. It didn't matter. The staff would have to separate us every day or we'd brutalise each other. However, I'd been paying attention to my enemy. He often teased a boy named Christopher, who liked Bionicle. With two things in common, I forged an alliance with Christopher.

Logan would try to control the bus. 'One, two, three. Everyone shut up,' he would say. To change that, I had an idea. We would all talk over him; it was a game called Invisible Logan. Everyone joined in, and though he would scream and threaten us, we persisted. I'd grin, replaying the memory in my mind. His suffering was my pleasure. It gave me power.

The only problem? Logan's mother ran the jigsaw club. Every Wednesday, the bus would drop some of us there. It took place in a secondary school, after the pupils there had gone home. There were biscuits, crisps, and plenty of Nintendo DSs'. It was a child's paradise. Logan would hit us or pull our ears. His mum wouldn't believe anyone, so he'd always get away with it. In Meadows, you earned the ire of either Logan or a TA called Brittany. Some, like me, earned it from both.

***

'Owen touched you by accident,' I said. Brittany had him up against the fence. Her foot was on his. There was no escape.

'Count to 100, I'll let him go,' she said. I counted 100 in the ten times table.

'Done, let him go.' She gritted her teeth, stomping on my foot. I winced. Now we were both trapped. 'I counted to 100. You didn't say how to do it.' She grinned, swiftly releasing us when Ciandra arrived. She crept to the other end of the playground, face pale. We'd tell the other staff what had happened, yet Brittany always had a valid explanation.

Some things hadn't changed, despite the change of environment. And I wasn't the only one who wished they could.

'Lucy, it's ridiculous,' grandma lectured. 'He'll be seven this year. The others don't wear nappies.'

Mum uttered something under her breath. 'Well,' she murmured, looking at me with narrowed eyes. 'Do you feel you don't need them?'

'Lucy, I'm not having this conversation again. He shouldn't wear them.'

'I look stupid in them,' I asserted. 'Sometimes I get to the toilet.'

'But you struggle at home,' mum said.

'Riley helps me go to the toilet. I'll be fine. And Ciandra says I'll be in integration soon.'

'You hear that, Lucy? He can't wear that in a proper classroom.'

'With integration he won't be in a mainstream class all the time.'

'Lucy, I don't want to hear it. He's not wearing them.'

No more constantly pulling my trousers up in school. I still wore nappies at night, but it was a step in the right direction. And nobody else needed to know. Besides, PE with Ciandra had strengthened me. The muscles in my buttocks weren't as stiff. Soon I would be in mainstream. I had already made the next push into Astronaut class.

As I progressed, lessons deviated slightly. We made vinegar volcanos in science. Riley, a teaching assistant, worked with me. She put aside time to teach me computing and helping to foster a newfound love of writing stories. My reading skills improved dramatically. Every day, I was trying something different.

Because of my anger, Ciandra suggested I undergo therapy after school. Dad found me counselling, where I showed my frustrations through LEGO whilst the therapist observed. My outbursts lessened, Ciandra didn't have to restrain me as much.

However, the therapist blamed my behaviours on mum and dad's parenting. She listed a vast number of medications for me to take in quick succession. According to dad, mum would often leave the parent counselling sessions in tears. Progress had been made since Blue House Primary, but the road ahead was paved with fierce obstacles all built to throw me far off course. It was that way for all the children in Meadows, I suppose. We all had our own unique challenges to overcome.

Despite this, Ciandra wanted us to enjoy our time in school, with trips to LEGOLAND and two nights at Citadel Woods, the first time I was away from my immediate family. Soon my first year in Meadows was over. Logan and Christopher left that summer. I turned seven, read most of Roald Dahl's books, amongst other works, enjoyed films, and listened to Arcade Fire with dad. In one year, my world had grown tremendously. After being outside the classroom for years, it was now time for me to return. Well, not quite – I'd still spend most of the day in Meadows, and Riley would accompany me to class. Would the other children tease me? Could I do the work? Will the teacher like me?

I had many preconceived notions. None of them came true. I got along with my classmates. None of them questioned it when Riley scribed for me. I enjoyed my lessons, often discussing the subject long after leaving class. I'd raise my hand and discuss the characters in a book during English.

Nobody expected me to, but I always wanted to attend class trips. I took part in school plays, learnt the violin with the rest of my class in music. Grandma still has pictures of me playing in a concert. Lessons in Meadows became repetitive. I'd realise we were doing the same things as last year.

In hindsight, I see Meadows as a bridge. Ciandra knew certain children could reintegrate. Some of us just needed an extra push, a bit more time to develop. At the end of the school year, she announced that two of my other friends and I would be in mainstream. A permanent move.

The three of us cheered, high-fiving. I glanced at Ciandra. She smiled back. *I'll make you proud.* But that wasn't the only announcement. The school was undergoing long-overdue renovations. Meadows would move into the main building. In its place would be an office and a nursery.

28.7.10

Dear Nick, Lucy and Max,

Thank you so much for the gift voucher, which I shall enjoy spending during the holidays. Your kind and truthful words addressed to us touched everyone. You managed to bring out the very ethos of Meadows, thank you.

It has been both rewarding and exciting to watch Max mature and develop. He is a very special boy who has overcome a great deal to be where he is today. Every step, however small, is a great achievement. Well done, Max. It has been a pleasure to work together with you, and thank you for your support.

Please keep in touch.

With love and best wishes, Ciandra

Chapter 4: Susan

Ciandra had dropped a bombshell. We knew about the construction work but not how it would affect Meadows. As for moving to mainstream full time, it's what I wanted. Integration had gone well the previous year, and Meadows was downstairs if I needed anything. My friends Owen and Alexander were in the year group above me. But I'd see them in the playground.

The entire thing would be a carefully framed transition, reflecting the immense progress I'd made in a short time. Given my willingness to wear prism-glasses, my eye-sight improved to where I no longer needed such a prescription. I had friends and knew the school. With help, I could make it to the toilet. Year four would be the school year I needed. A reintroduction then onto better things.

I stepped onto the bus that first morning and darted past a new passenger. This boy? His name was Matthew, a tall figure with hooded eyes and sharp cornrows. He wasn't new to the school, and every child avoided him. I wasn't keen to learn why, especially after the glare he aimed at five-year-old Henry. Poor kid, first day and already a target.

We arrived in the back playground; construction work would render the front unusable for some time. Henry went with Ciandra, while Alexander and Owen were shown to their class by another TA. Riley had taken time off Meadows to support me for the first few mornings.

Many Meadows staff I'd known had left. Construction work closed some parts of the school. However, my teacher seemed nice enough, offering to bring in his childhood LEGO for the children to play with. We were Walrus class. I could get used to that. We had school lunches, and so long as I spoke to Riley, the noise in the cafeteria was a minor nuisance. In the afternoon, it was time to meet my new teaching assistants in the hall upstairs.

The moment we arrived, something pushed against my chest. I glanced up, finding a rotund woman entrenched in my personal space. Her eyes were blocks of jagged ice. They scrutinised me, following my every movement. Her clothes were weathered with stretch marks, her hair enclosed in a cruel bun. A harsh, vigorous tap pounded my shoulder.

'Aren't you going to speak, Grotty?' she probed. Her rotten breath pierced my nostrils. Even Riley turned away.

'It's impolite to ignore someone when you meet them.'

I withheld my breath, cheeks puffed out.

'Have they have taught him social skills?'

'Yes, he has had some speech and language therapy,' Riley replied.

'Do you have a name, Grotty?'

'Um... My name's Max.'

She leaned closer, towering over us. 'Speak louder, I'm going deaf. It happens when you get old and grey.'

'My name's Max.'

She groaned, 'Pay attention, Grotty.' Her voice lowered to a whisper, 'Do I talk like this? Like a mouse?'

I shook my head, ducking under her breath. She raised her voice. 'Or do I talk like this. Hello, Max, my name is Susan.'

Within milliseconds, I'm forced into a sweaty, steel handshake.

'See Riley, he's learning already. We'll do just fine.' She stepped aside, revealing another woman behind her. 'I want you to introduce yourself to this lovely lady. Don't be shy, do it.'

'Um, my name is Max. What's yours?'

'Hello, Max, my name is Karen. Pleased to meet you.'

'Shake her hand,' Susan ordered.

One awkward handshake and short-lived goodbye to Riley later, I was in Susan's iron grasp. Until we sat in class, it was as though I were on a leash. We were the only ones there. Lunchtime wasn't over yet.

'Pay attention,' she barked. *Are you Miss Trunchbull?* 'I will get a whiteboard. If you move, there will be consequences.' She tapped the back of her head. 'I've got eyes here.'

Soon she returned with a whiteboard and marker. 'Can you read?'

'Yes.'

One hand obstructed my potential escape; the other wrote a list of rules.

'Read it!'

'Always listen, no inappropriate behaviour, no shouting, don't run off.' I paused, noting a crudely drawn face, eyes popping out of its sockets. 'I can't read that.'

'Do you understand this?'

I nodded.

'Make poor choices and I will punish them with consequences.'

'What are the consequences?'

She smirked, almost viciously. 'You'll see. But I'd rather we don't have to go there.'

Throughout every lesson, Susan dominated. Move my leg? A hard tap on the shoulder. Not looking at the board? She'd ensure I did. But Susan wasn't all I had to worry about. Matthew smiled whenever he tripped Henry up on the bus. Would I be next? I couldn't be next. So I devised a plan.

OK, not a plan; I chose self-preservation. I bullied Henry and befriended Matthew. It was a choice between the lesser of two evils, as Henry was no pushover himself. He had altercations with just about everyone, and on one occasion quite literally drop-kicked a toddler. I had to choose between a thrashing from a five-year-old slightly taller than me or a pummelling from a giant. Neither were favourable, though one was certainly worse. Which is not to say I enjoyed sitting next to Matthew. He'd undo my seatbelt, get me beaten up by Henry. My predicament was the living definition of "caught between a rock and a hard place." But at least it meant that Owen didn't get bullied. I had protected my friend.

At lunchtimes, Susan had us sit away from my classmates. We'd be with the younger children. I couldn't say a word. And they'd all look at her with twinkling eyes as she told them about the rural town she grew up in. She smiled at everyone, always striking up a conversation. But nobody knew about her ultimate weapon to deter me from "misbehaving": the Sensory Room.

***

'You're not focusing' Susan huffed, pulling my head up.

'I'm listening. I'm just tired.'

'This is your warning, Grotty. Pay attention.'

I rested my head on the desk, trying to avoid her breath. A hand clasped my back, ripping me from my chair. Everyone gaped, watching a one-sided battle unfold. I kicked and scratched, screaming until my throat turned raw. Susan was a bulldozer, relentless. She held me like a dirty rag and dragged me through the school. She tossed me into the Sensory Room and slammed the door.

34

Pitch-black darkness. They called it a sensory room but turning on the light switch almost blinded you. Padded white walls and a padded white floor. I may as well have worn a straitjacket. No hot, no cold , no time. Just me and the darkness until the light went on, with Susan outside the whole time.

Scream, cry, kick the door. It didn't matter. Susan remained in control. If she felt it necessary, I'd spend the whole of lunchtime in there. My food would be outside, and I'd watch through a tiny window as it grew cold. Other adults? She'd strike up a conversation with them, diverting their attention away from me. *Why does she hate me?* Sometimes, people forgot I was in there. It was hours, with just my thoughts and imagination for comfort.

Swear in frustration? Sensory Room. Look at someone in an "unkind way"? Sensory Room. Any reason, any hour, any day. People knew the room existed, but assumed it was only ever used in "extreme circumstances", and as an eight-year-old I didn't have the capacity to argue that it was "used unfairly" in my case.

And whilst there were bruises and carpet burns on my legs and knees, the damage wasn't intentionally caused by Susan. Rather it was the result of the resistance I put up in our almost daily conflicts. Besides, kids often get bruises in the playground. And speaking of which, you'd think it a child's dream to be there. I could socialise with whoever

I wanted. So joining Susan on her frolic with the younger children would be made up for right?

Children whizzing by like bullets, their playful screams endless and deafening. Basketballs pulverised my face every other minute. If I tried to leave, a staff member pulled me to the Sensory Room. So not much of a dream come true for me. One incident involved Brittany from Meadows. They had their own separate playground. But on that day she had led the children into the mainstream one. Henry and I got into an escalation, and she intervened, siding with him. Before I knew it, she had me on my backside, striking me several times in the buttocks. A good old-fashioned spanking. To escape, I had to roll onto the concrete.

'Bring him back, Henry,' she called. A chase ensued. Henry grabbed a ball. Having cornered me, he socked me in the face with it. Laughing as I cried. When Susan discovered the commotion, she took me to the Sensory Room without a word. Why? Because I lied about her friend Brittany.

There weren't any consequences for Henry. He successfully convinced Susan that I'd "punched him", meaning his retaliation was "justified".

In a way, the Sensory Room was better than the playground, I preferred being alone with my thoughts to the unbearable chaos out there. For that reason, I'd purposefully cause escalations with Susan to avoid the playground. Yes, sometimes I'd get to hang out with Owen and

Alexander. But it was impossible to hear them over everything else. People ask me why I flinch around balls. That playground is why.

I started referring to members of staff as animals or other objects. For example, I called my class teacher a clock. Most didn't mind, and some even embraced it. I think I did this to disguise the environment I was in. Hiding behind the persona of "weird kid" was easier than confronting my anxieties.

One minute I was in Meadows with Riley and Ciandra. The next I was in Susan's charge. She was the only one I never vocally referred to as an object or animal. But in my mind, she was always Miss Trunchbull, the fearsome headteacher from Roald Dahl's book *Matilda*. For whatever reason, though, I dubbed Karen a chicken.

'You're a cute chicken,' I chirped. Karen glared, pushing me into a chair. I probed the back of my head.

'Sit down and behave.' She forcibly planted me into the seat. 'You like chickens? Because chickens go peck.' Her fingernails were daggers planted into my flesh. 'Peck. Peck. Peck.' Jab, jab, jab. I roared in pain. It hurt to move my hands. I attempted to fight back, only to face reprisal. She grinned, slapping me with my own hands. 'Why are you hitting yourself? Don't hit yourself.'

Later, grandma found a few small cuts on my fingers. 'What happened?' she asked.

'Karen scratched me.'

'I'm sure it was an accident.'

I shook my head.

'She has a lot to worry about, Max. She probably didn't notice.'

Karen strode around the school with well-kempt hair and almost business-like confidence. She was a chatty, youthful woman who spoke like the Queen and never seemed the type to cause harm. As my resentment toward her grew, I found ways to retaliate. Whenever she bent over, I'd climb onto her back. I wasn't a heavy-weight, but I'd ingrain my hands into her hair and pull. All this happened in front of other, disapproving members of staff, as I proudly exclaimed that I was 'riding a chicken', believing she wouldn't dare do me physical harm so publicly in the way she had done so previously when no one else had been looking.

Besides, I had a "diagnosis"; weird behaviour was one of my "quirks". Really, it was just revenge and a way of escaping PE, the only lesson I hated. I would invariably get thrashed in dodgeball.

To catch up physically, I needed "occupational therapy", Susan's idea of which was climbing to the top of an apparatus that leant against the wall outside our class-room. Rising a good fifteen or twenty feet up in the air, it would shake when I climbed it. I always thought it would fall over and crush me. Twice a day was my regimen, with Susan always at the bottom.

'I can't do it. I will fall,' I whimpered.

'Nonsense, kick out the T,' Susan called. She climbed up on the bars next to me, practically holding me hostage until I got to the top.

Such were some of the challenges of my schooldays, which is not to say I didn't have favourite subjects. I enjoyed history, IT, creative writing. At my parents' request, Susan taught me to touch-type. To this day, I can't write more than a few words by hand. And if I hadn't learnt, I wouldn't be writing this book. In fact, the rate at which I learnt impressed even Susan, albeit not enough to gain her trust.

But let's fast-forward a little. The construction work was complete. They had replaced haggard Meadows with steel and concrete. I was running errands to the new office with another pupil, after a suggestion made by one "professional" I had regular appointments with. On the way back to class, we encountered another pupil, who couldn't have been older than six.

There were two of us. But her attention was on me. 'You're creepy. And ugly too.'

'Fuck off!' I retorted.

She laughed, repeating my words. Somehow, Molly, my classmate, convinced me to walk away. Later, on the playground, an arm struck my shoulder, then someone pulled my coat. I blinked, suppressing the tears in my eyes. *Ignore them.*

'Did you see his face?' another student laughed.

'Max,' Molly said, pointing out a group of children. Amongst them was the girl who'd insulted me earlier. 'We should tell Susan.'

Hands clenched fists, I charged forward. They scattered, laughing. Was I just a toy to them? Something to play with? Rage was my fuel, visions of slaughtering them consumed my mind.

'Ha ha, ugly,' the girl jabbed. Her friends abandoned her, bunching up together like cornered rats.

'Last warning. Say sorry,' I demanded.

She laughed like a chipmunk, undeterred.

Before she could escape, I encased her face in my claws. One hand dismantled her hair, the other sought to pry her skin off. Screams engulfed the playground. Everyone stopped to stare in horror. Susan and Karen to the rescue. They yanked me across the bone-piercing concrete. Into the Sensory Room where I belonged.

'You're in here because you hurt Afua. Do you understand?' Susan explained.

'Yes, but she hurt me first. Molly saw it.'

'Uh-uh, Grotty, let me finish. We will sort it out. Now apologise and we'll leave.'

'Sorry.'

She took me to a corridor where Karen was waiting with the girl. Crude cuts had indented her face. 'Max, this is Afua, and she's feeling upset' Susan stated. Afua smirked.

'She's grinning, I don't think she's—'

'I'm not finished, it's rude to interrupt people.' She had me sit down. 'Afua, when Max hurt you, how did it make you feel?'

'Very sad.'

Susan glanced at Karen, motioning her to speak. 'Max, when you hurt people and say unkind things. It makes them sad.'

'That's right, it's very unkind to hurt others,' Susan added. 'Karen and I are friends. When we have a problem, we talk about it.' She towered over me. 'Don't you think you and Afua should do the same?' I nodded, hoping she'd leave. 'Afua, how do you feel?'

'Sad,' she replied, occasionally peering at the floor.

'Do you think Max is unkind?' asked Susan.

'Yes.' A wide grin escaped her mouth.

'This is bull,' I interjected. 'Your friends hit me, you said—'

Susan grabbed hold of my face. 'Shall I take you to the Sensory Room?'

'Ask Molly, she—'

'Uh-uh, Grotty, I'm talking.' She paced around the corridor, 'Afua, did you hurt Max?'

'No, we were playing. Nobody saw him.'

'Max sometimes we have accidents on the playground,' remarked Karen. They made me apologise twice. Because Susan said I sounded "cross" the first time. Afua had won, period. If I tried anything else, I'd be back in the Sensory Room. I didn't want to miss out on creative writing. In my piece that day, Afua received the personification of a "demon" who terrorised whole villages. Susan enjoyed the story but failed to recognise that the character placating the beast was inspired by her.

Chapter 5: When Meadows Wither

I suppose this all raises a question: Where were Riley and Ciandra? Ciandra had her hands full. Experienced staff were leaving. There was the new building. She couldn't micromanage everything. Riley was training to become a teacher and had her job in Meadows. Sometimes we'd work together when Susan and Karen weren't available.

At the end of the last academic year they left. Ciandra retired, Riley took on her teaching course. Not only that, White Mountain's headmistress moved schools, too. Jemma, the deputy head, had temporarily taken her position. Almost all of the people who had previously made up my school life were absent, and I was left with Susan and Karen. On the bright side, Matthew ended his primary schooling. Therefore, there was no reason to antagonise Henry anymore. I even apologised for the year before and befriended him. We had something in common, after all. They often locked us in the Sensory Room.

Without Ciandra, the SENCO looked to Susan, who advocated for the Sensory Room. This left staff with a dilemma. If two children were misbehaving one would have to leave the Sensory Room. Susan solved this by finding the most seldom-used rooms, with the least people around. She practically converted certain parts of the school into make-shift dungeons.

More time in tiny rooms meant less in class. I tried to learn the violin. Susan would hold my head and obstruct the playing position I found comfortable. In my dad's words, "It was like she had a noose around you." It wasn't just my body they held hostage. In the first weeks of term I bought in the book *Holes*, by Louis Sachar. If I was on "best behaviour, Susan permitted fifteen minutes of reading time. If I weren't, she'd hide the book. I never brought in another after I finished with it. I feared she would steal them. In class, I'd have daydreams. All of them were about Susan and Karen repeatedly dying in grotesque ways. With visions of murder in my mind, I often tried acting on them.

I'd lunge for Susan, bringing the lesson to a halt. Soon after, I'd be in the Sensory Room, sobbing myself dry. I wanted a return to the distant days of Meadows. But in Ciandra's replacement, all I saw was a woman who browsed the internet and devoured cheeseburgers. Meadows had withered, a shell of its former self. I didn't want to accept that, but I had to.

***

'Midget,' a boy jabbed. A stab of horror rocked my chest. Pulled from my daydream, back into the concrete and rain. He bounced the ball upwards; I threw my hands in front of my face.

'What's the matter, don't you like balls? .
come you're so short? You look like a baby.'

'Fuck... fuck off.' A great tremor of tear:
whelmed me, some escaping as I closed my eyes. Foo
running. When I peered out, he had fled. Other chil
were rushing over, pointing me out to Susan.

'He's crying,' one child remarked.

'Are you OK?' asked another.

'I'll take it from here,' said Susan. 'Come on, Grotty, let's go.'

I didn't resist. She led me to the Sensory Room.
I didn't want to leave. The tremors shook me to my core.
Thoughts of murder, killing the boy in front of his parents.
I couldn't escape them, I wanted to hurt him. I needed to
hurt him.

Lunchtime, he was in front of me in the queue. Revenge. I grabbed a cutlery knife, stabbing him through his
jumper. His face went ghost-white, eyes fading.

'No!' Susan roared. Veins frozen, I pointed the
knife at her chest. Jaw clenched, she squeezed my arm. The
knife crashed to the floor with a clang.

Everyone gaped, then more staff arrived. Soon the
threw me in the Sensory Room. I was excluded for three day

***

'I have students and staff wondering why he's s
here,' Jemma told mum. In her position as acting head,

45

recommended sending me to an out-of-borough correctional unit. From what I've been told, Susan supported the idea. A sympathetic ear in the local authority stood up for me. Without her, they'd have sent me away from my family. I got lucky that time.

***

The bell blared off as usual, but I remained where I was. Face pressed against the wall, concealing my tears.

'Oi, Grotty, time to go inside,' Susan ordered.

Head bowed, I plodded towards the gate.

'You're not going anywhere.' She grasped my shoulders; I didn't resist. 'Do you want the Sensory Room?'

'No, I want to kill myself.'

Her eyes narrowed. She pulled me over to a bench. 'Max, that makes me very sad.'

I pointed to a nearby puddle. 'I want to drown myself. But there isn't enough water.'

'Why do you want to kill yourself? I don't understand.'

'I want to kill myself. I want to kill myself,' I repeated.

The school caretaker walked past. 'Are you feeling sad, Max?'

'Yes. I want to kill myself.' I stood up, but Susan wrestled me into her arms, squeezing tightly.

'If I kill myself, I can't come back. Do you get that?'

'You're a special boy, Max,' she consoled.

***

Dad held me in the car as earth-shattering sobs tore through my chest.

'There were two girls,' I began. 'The big one hit me with... with a broom. They said they'd take me to a children's home.' Of course, nobody had hit me with a broom; a series of cascading events was what had caused my breakdown. But unable to find words at that age to explain my predicament, I conjured a fake story.

Later in the term, Susan compelled me to attend a residential trip, telling me I'd have to go to the Sensory Room if I refused. There was watery hot chocolate, and sharing a room with six noisy boys, as well as peer activities I wouldn't normally dream of doing. On the second day at 5 a.m., I sneaked out of the boys' dorm and stole a teacher's phone.

'Help, I'm in prison,' I screamed, calling my parents. Soon the teachers had wrestled me to the ground. Susan had me run laps around the fields afterward, albeit she insisted it was nothing more than occupational therapy. By the time we got back inside, I was a wheezing, snotty mess. Thankfully, my parents had packed an inhaler.

11.3.12

(A letter addressed from me to Susan)

Look I'm not having you anymore so just read what I say to you. I know why you wont harm me when someone else is in the room. Here's why because you will be fired by Jemma and become homeless I know your little act. People may think your nice but your horrible and do not care about anything or anyone.

I also think u need to stop hurting my feelings. So just stop and think about others or you will become like the horrible aunts in James and the giant peach. Your mean but you can change that by stopping all the things your doing. Ok I hope you have learnt ur lesson. From max ps no rubbing this out. I wont do work today.

Apologies for the atrocious grammar and spelling. I wanted to preserve the letter's authenticity. The events leading up to it don't differ from the cycle I've described so far. But I'll fill in the blanks with what is noteworthy. Karen wanted to undertake teacher training. They replaced her with Cody, who never sent me to the Sensory Room.

If I did all my work, we would play games on his phone together. It lasted for a few months until he left to become a teacher. Zoe replaced him. She made use of the Sensory Room but preferred removing my socks and having me stand outside in the rain. Amid it all, my parents met Jenny. Still in university, she'd be with me in the school holidays when they were working. For my birthday the year before, Dad had bought me a computer. It had a disc drive but no games. Jenny changed that, introducing me to Age of Empires III. That and later The Settlers: Rise of an

Empire were all I played. For the first time, my LEGO sat dormant on the shelf. I would fantasise about the battles I had created and the cites I built in the Sensory Room. Video games were a world where Susan couldn't follow.

"When's Jenny coming over?" I must have asked that question a thousand times.

Summer term, we finally got a new headmistress, but she didn't affect my situation for better or worse and was more of a presence than anything else. Outside of school, doctors were concerned about how underweight I was and wanted me on a feeding tube. This possibility caused me to have recurring nightmares. In each one, faceless figures restrained me whilst a metal tube punctured my brain. Mum and dad fought to their last breath against the treatment and fortunately succeeded. We never stepped into that clinic again.

**

'I've just carried thirty,' I caterwauled. 'It's bullshit.'

Susan peered up from her phone. 'Don't swear, Grotty.'

'Do it yourself. It's your raffle,' I grumbled, storming off. Thirty 1.5 litre bottles for the school fair, all of them bigger than me. And now, she wanted me to carry another five? No thanks.

She dashed over, propelling me backward. 'It's this or the Sensory Room.'

49

You're her slave. Kill her. I galloped, throwing a punch. She caught it, we're locked in a struggle of strength.

'All your choice, Grotty,' she reprimanded. 'You'll be in the Sensory Room after home time.'

I shrieked in fury, ramming my nails into her arm. Her face turned a pale white, veins peering through.

'You're getting stronger,' she mused. Rage-filled red engulfed her face. 'But you've made a poor choice.'

Zoe jolted toward us, yanking me away. 'He's too angry for the Sensory Room,' Susan fumed. 'Take him to the office.'

A brutal, one-sided battle continued. Four against one. Even Karen got in on the action. Finally, they forced me into a tiny room with boarded-up windows. I winced, unable to wipe away cascading sweat, clutching strands of Susan's hair in my hands.

'He's like a little animal,' one of them laughed. They took it in turns, pressing me to the carpet, my eyes watering as I tasted whatever putrid things lay down there.

'Give up,' Susan seethed, grasping my head. A shower of tears, kicking, screaming. All were in vain.

'I'm gonna kill your fucking family,' I boomed.

'In your dreams, Grotty.'

'I've been waiting ages,' dad fumed. Zoe stood in his way, shielding the ongoing struggle. 'However angry he is I'll handle it, just let me take him home.'

'No, he's not ready.'

'You said that five minutes ago.' He pushed past and discovered us. My head fell to the floor with a thud. Glassy-eyed, the TAs glanced at each-other. Nobody said a word. Dad picked me up under his arm and took us home.

'You're lucky your twit father was there,' Susan remarked the next day. 'He spoils you rotten.'

We couldn't afford a solicitor. And if my parents wanted to contest a place in their chosen secondary school, they'd need support from White Mountain. I had to survive another year.

Chapter 6: Evaporation

What exactly had evaporated? And what would evaporate? The few friends I had? Gone. Meadows? Already withered. The school itself? Slowly changing, old rooms refurbished, others boarded up. But I wasn't dealing with a mere physical absence. After three years with Susan, I'd soon have to face whatever lay beyond. Or in more specific terms, secondary school.

Compared to much of the rest of what life has in store for us, it's a familiar, orderly movement. Children grow up. Moving to a bigger school is part of that ordeal. But for me, at age ten, it seemed a hellish destination. Potential school bullies. Flung into the maddening rush on the stairs, and possibly a worse version of Susan. I knew an abyss was forming, I'd have to jump to the next stage in life. Besides, could I survive another year at White Mountain? These were all subconscious thoughts and too much for a ten-year-old.

My bus was replaced with a crammed cab, the escort I'd known for five years moved on, all my friends left. Suddenly, I was the oldest and the only verbal child there.

Concentrate hard and listen to the radio. Or suffer ear-piercing shrieking and dodge the uncontrolled flapping of hands, which never made for a pleasant journey. Beyond that, these children were a reminder. Whereas my time in primary school had almost elapsed, theirs was just beginning.

For now, I watched the cars, head pressed against the window in a tiny cab. "Kids in America" by Kim Wilde played in the background, barely audible over infantile screeching. It's a wonder I never got slapped accidentally. At least video games awaited me at home.

I struck a deal with Susan to avoid the playground. I'd agree to choose classmates, and they'd "hang out" with me at lunchtime. I made them laugh and enjoyed it when they did, but never had the courage to form a lasting friendship beyond the moments Susan put us together. Mostly, it just got me out of the Sensory Room, and Susan could say she had "helped develop my social skills".

Appeasement became my main policy. Making tea for Susan and the other staff was easier than fighting an unwinnable struggle. By the time term was over, I had led two of my peers in writing, directing and performing a chocolate commercial, as well as entering and losing the school Christmas card competition. I also knew the amount of milk Susan preferred in her tea.

In the new year, my parents set me up with an occupational therapist near the school. Every Wednesday, Susan and I embarked on a lengthy walk there. Buses were available, but she preferred half an hour down a steep hill. I'd imagine finding money in the street.

'You're not that lucky,' Susan laughed.

When the fabled day came, and I found a five-pound note, Susan snatched the money from my hands, pocketing it. So much for hot chocolate on a frosty-morning expedition. Our new headmistress saw I wasn't meeting the attendance criteria and sent my parents a strongly worded letter. I'd miss a few more days at school than most. Either I would have an appointment to attend or my meagre immune system got into a brutal conflict with a virus.

After explaining my diagnosis, mum and dad got off with a slap on the wrist. With the SAT exams and secondary school approaching, I suppose it wasn't worth the argument.

***

'You will go to Crown Heights School,' dad began.

'Um, right,' I muttered.

'Don't worry, there's a special needs provision.' I crossed and uncrossed my arms and legs, unsure of what position I preferred.

'Autism's a label, it's a passport to places like Meadows.'

'Uh... yes.'

'It's called Portum. I think its Latin for something. Sounds interesting.'

'Yeah.'

Me, being a miniature scrap of flesh and bone would not fare well in secondary school. Dad said the other children had threatened to tie him to a flagpole on his first day of year seven. If that were how it was for him without a label, then surely it would be 100 times worse for me. I suffered a lot of nightmares in the lead-up to my "visitation" days.

***

'I need to use the toilet,' I begged. 'I need to go now.' Susan ignored me, tightening her grip on the Sensory Room door. I jumped up and down, banged on the door, begged. Despite it all Susan still sat browsing Facebook. I had two choices: wet myself and commit social suicide or relieve myself in a room I hated. A corner selected, lip tightly curled. I chose the second option.

Upon discovering it, Susan's eyebrows furrowed. 'No, that is totally inappropriate! You do not act like an animal. Do you understand me?'

She wrenched me upstairs, bringing me before the headmistress. My explanation of "being afraid" didn't matter. They made me clean it. By the time I left school that day, it was nearing five o'clock. Whilst doing research for this book, through reading the emails sent to my parents at the time, I learnt that they had already cleaned the floor. The only reason I had to stay after school was to "face a consequence".

***

'We're meeting your teacher for parents' evening,' mum said

'Ask her if I'm a valued member of the class,' I interjected, words falling out of my mouth. 'Never mind.'

'Is everything all right, darling?'

'I'm fine mum. Forget it.'

'If there's something wrong you can tell us.'

'I'm going upstairs.'

I didn't want to go there. Talking to mum about my inner fears felt like being coddled. Besides, a bigger problem emerged. Susan believed having the word "sex" in my vocabulary meant I'd been accessing pornography on the internet. I let the word slip during a school day, and dad ended up in the headmistress's office with the police.

Susan and other staff had raised a safeguarding concern and felt mum and dad weren't responsible-enough parents. Dad had to retell my entire developmental history before they let him go.

***

'We can't trust the school anymore,' he told mum. I peered through the keyhole, listening in on their conversation.

'It's ridiculous,' mum said. 'They pulled you out of work for it.'

Why would Susan do that? I did nothing wrong. As I lay in bed that night, I thought back to year four, then further back to Blue House Primary. *Everyone always hates me.*

A clenched fist trembled in the air before tears soaked my bedsheets. Would secondary school be the same?

The day before my first "visit", I had another nightmare. All throughout, I trembled like Oliver Twist asking for more gruel. The school a behemoth, the students giants.

'Are you nervous, Grotty?' Susan asked.

'Yeah, a bit.'

'Ah, you'll be fine. Stand up straight.' She corrected my posture, but it didn't last more than a second. 'Never mind,' she said, after we had climbed around three flights of narrow stairs.

We arrived at the stair landing. We barely noticed the steps leading to Portum, the school's autism provision. Silhouette portraits of each student on one side, entrance on the other.

'Here we go, Grotty.'

Last steps of my life. I glanced around. Though larger than Meadows, it was a mere series of different-sized rooms connected by small corridors. Susan turned me around. Awaiting us was a woman.

'Welcome, we're so very lucky to have you both.'

She led us into a common room, referred to, quite literally, as the "kitchen", because that was what it was. Really, it doubled as both common room and kitchen, being a large-enough area for the students to eat lunch and socialise. A sliding door led to a "garden", in reality a bit of fake grass, pots with withered soil, and a punching bag. The woman introduced herself as Charlotte, offering me chocolate muffins and pineapple juice.

'Your parents said they're your favourite.'

I scoffed down a mouthful.

'Well, Grotty, what do you say?'

'Thank you,' I muttered in between mouthfuls.

'Good enough,' Susan said listlessly.

'Right, would you like me to tell you about Portum?' Charlotte asked. I gave a late nod.

'We named all the rooms after famous people with autism,' she said. 'Turing, Einstein.' She listed them all. And the pieces of artwork littering the walls? All made by students. She regaled me with every detail.

***

'Nice to meet you,' I murmured, participating in a sweaty handshake with two Portum pupils. *Please don't kill me.* With a teaching assistant to help them, they would give me a "student perspective" on Portum, albeit they often talked amongst themselves and forgot about me, quavering in the opposite seat.

'I'm sending you off early to avoid the rush on the stairs. Our students don't like it,' Charlotte said. 'See you next week.' *Run.*

'Let's go Susan, I'm tired.'

'Fair dos, Grotty, you've had a long day.'

We both bolted, crowds of screaming teenagers just metres behind us. *Do I have to come back? I can't do five years here.* Next visit, we were in the "Big Room". It had an actual name. But being the largest room in Portum, everyone just called it that. Shabby blue carpet, a table full of art supplies. Various game consoles, DVDs, a television.

Inside the room was my cohort; like me they were all with their respective TAs. Charlotte left us in the care of Lucas, one of the teaching assistants at Portum. Dad said there were only four highly contested places available. Lucas would see me and three other boys through a coveted initiation.

Lucas explained that every Portum student created a silhouette portrait. In the distant future, when our time at Portum ended, we'd take them with us as a reflection of our journey. One by one, Lucas guided us through the process. He took a picture of our faces, then traced around them.

I chose purple for my background, red for the silhouette. Susan raised a tight-lipped frown, observing me and Lucas working together. She tried offering input, but I ignored it. Only when we had finished could she take a picture on her phone.

Charlotte smiled, admiring all the portraits. 'They're so special.'

This time our cohort left an hour before the crowds flooded out. A welcome change.

***

'You're going to have an operation,' dad informed. 'The doctors want to check your gut.'

'Oh,' I whispered, biting my lip.

'Don't worry. It's only for a night.'

A colonoscopy and an endoscopy. What fun! My last meal was a sandwich from Costa Coffee. Once inside the hospital they only allowed me to drink water. The aim was to find the cause of my toileting issues. Before the operation, I had to drink a rancid medicine at different points in the day. I jerked it back, eyes scrunched up. Like ingesting acid, it sterilised my tongue. Clutching my stomach, I limped into bed, though it occurred to me I'd have been better off sleeping on the floor. Concrete sheets, sweltering summer heat. Somehow, dad and I survived the night.

'You're first,' the nurse said. *Shit!* After donning a scratchy hospital gown, I was led downstairs, between walls painted a copious white. Masked doctors forced a plastic mask on my face. I screamed and screamed the harder they pressed. Dad convinced them to delay the operation. There were three options: two forms of general anaesthetic that would put me to sleep – the sleeping mask I'd already rejected; and a medicine that tasted like sweetened rat poison, or so I imagined – or a local anaesthetic, a numbing cream they'd give me so I wouldn't feel anything.

'Get it over with now,' grandma advised. 'Then you can put it behind you.' Drenched in sweat, I chose the anaesthetic. Mum and grandma distracted me with *Where's Wally?* while the doctors made their investigation. Fortunately, they found nothing wrong. If I had to take a guess, I'd say my difficulties were down to a lack of strength in the muscles.

One of the hospital staff suggested Docusate, a laxative. My parents mixed a tasteless liquid form in hot chocolate. I didn't even notice a difference in the taste. And what's more, it worked! For years afterwards, the Docusate did the work my muscles couldn't. I had toilet-trained myself and not a moment too soon. Though I hadn't suffered an "accident" in some time, I knew I couldn't afford to take any chances in secondary school.

***

July 3rd, 2013, induction day at Crown Heights School. Outside the gate, mum had her hands on my shoulders. I grimaced, shaking like a shot pigeon. Shielded under her arms, we went inside. All the teenagers could see me, the tiny boy coddled by his mummy. I bowed my head. *Please don't look at me, please don't look at me.*

Mum left me in Portum, where Charlotte gave me a bowl of Cheerios for breakfast. I scrutinised every student who passed, legs begging to run away.

'You were top of school in year six,' the teacher said, addressing me and other upcoming year sevens. 'Now you're at the bottom. Little children all over again.' *Little. I'm so fucked.*

Inside the den of my fears, there was no choice. I took part in everything.

'He's such a trooper,' Charlotte told dad when he collected me.

**

A brave new world, the current equilibrium left to evaporate. No more therapy, I didn't have to wear glasses, I was toilet-trained. No more primary school, no more Susan.

Finally, there was time to relax and play Minecraft for the summer. A LEGO figure toppled off the shelf. I spun around to find Susan standing in by bedroom.

'Oh, I'm so sorry. I'll put him back up,' she said. 'How are you, Grotty?' I'd forgotten she was coming. 'Are you surprised?'

She ordered me downstairs. She had come to help us find a bicycle. If I learnt to ride, it would help my motor skills.

'I need to go to the toilet,' I blurted, rushing off.

'You have two minutes,' Susan called. Panting, I locked myself in the bathroom. *No way out.* 'It's all about firm structure and boundaries.'

'Right, I see,' mum said.

'Works with my daughter. You're both too soft with Max. How do you think my parents kept our shop going?' *No choice.*

She banged on the door. 'Come on. We have places to be.' With bated breath, I trudged out. She marched mum and I to the bike shop and back. Nothing came of it; I had no desire to learn.

Susan stuck her tongue out, leaving us outside the bus stop. 'Mum, I don't want to see her again. Ever.'

'It's a shame, she really liked you.'

I sighed. 'That bitch always threw me in the Sensory Room. Funny way of showing it.'

'She didn't understand.'

'She understands, she just doesn't care.' An invisible force seized my throat. 'Let's just go home.'

Chapter 7: Secondary School

September 3rd 2013, a thorn of fear embedded in my stomach, I type the following into YouTube. "How to survive secondary school?" I found a video from a recent graduate.

'Don't worry, they're not gonna throw you in the bin,' she said.

I sighed, looking at myself in the window. Dad said I was so thin he could see my ribcage. *I'm dead meat tomorrow.*

Tomorrow was a transition day, just year seven on the premises. The idea being to get them used to the school before the older children are unleashed. *If not tomorrow then the day after tomorrow. I'll end up being bullied by the first week, the second at a push. What if they grab me by the straps on my new purple schoolbag? What If I'm beaten senseless in a corridor? I'm basically powerless, I can't do jackshit about it.*

Too proud to show weakness, I voiced none of my concerns, albeit putting on a brave face didn't matter. The day after transition, I clung to the sofa for dear life. My hands were coated in sweat. 'Max, if you don't get off the sofa, I'm carrying you to the bus myself,' dad warned.

I rushed to the bus the second he said that.

So far, I'd met Lucas, and he seemed nice enough, showing me around Portum and asking what video games I played. Arthur, a TA as new to the school as me, had a juvenile sense of humour that always made me roar with laughter. I tiptoed onto the bus. The older boys were playing on their Nintendo 3DSs'. *Don't look at them. Don't even brush against them.*

'Are you nervous?' the bus escort asked. Unable to conjure a response, I pretended not to hear. The other boys, all older, towered above me. *Do I really belong here?*

For the first two days, Lucas and Charlotte escorted me to Portum. On the third day, I was all on my own. The other boys would all make their usual journey to Portum. There were two options: freeze and get pushed onto the concrete or brave the journey to Portum. I shadowed the other boys, hoping they'd protect me. Upon entering Portum, Charlotte took me aside. 'Well done, it can't have been easy. You know quite a lot of our students don't like the noise.'

'Um, thanks,' I replied.

'Normally, we go to Citadel Woods this year. Like you did with Ciandra. She's a good friend of mine. Do you have a message for her?'

'Tell her I'm doing well.'

'OK, I will. This year, we forgot to book Citadel Woods.'

'Oh.'

'But your mum told us about Wood House, isn't that fantastic?'

'Hmm.'

'And I was wondering if you'd like to come.' *Great, thanks mum.*

'Uh, no thanks.'

'Oh, why not?'

I'd been in the school less than a week, and genuinely expected to be ambushed at any moment. And here Charlotte was asking me to spend nights away with boisterous pupils I barely knew. Yeah, not gonna happen.

'Is it because we're not going to Citadel Woods?' she asked. 'Don't worry. It will only be people from Portum.'

'No, I... I just don't wanna go.'

'You don't have to go. But perhaps you'll change your mind later. Shall I ask you again?'

I nodded.

'OK. Lucas will take you to period one today. I'll speak to you later.' Lucas and I made our way through the rat run they called school. We endured mortar rounds of boisterous screaming. Every other second someone bumped into me. I maintained a tight grip of the stair railings.

In the mainstream school, being with a TA painted a target on my back. Their presence meant the mainstream pupils knew I had "something wrong with me". In my mind, those outside Portum existed on two extremes. They either thought we were "retarded" or they patronised us out of fear of causing offence. Any alternative view was inconceivable to me. I was an emotionally unintelligent eleven-year-old who had spent most of his life in rooms by himself. Social interactions with peers were usually done in a controlled environment.

Today I was to attend an "introductions event" in the library. Teachers wanted us year sevens to get acquainted. And potentially to make friends with each other. I pressed my head against the table, ears covered, refusing to look up. Just me and Lucas, segregated together.

'Max, what are your hobbies?' the teacher asked.

Lucas gently tapped me on the shoulder. I peered up, my body becoming a vessel of heat. All the other children were looking, some of them whispering amongst themselves. I'm the "autistic kid", what am I going to say? Can I speak or am I "retarded?"

'Um... I like gaming.'

What the hell was that? I retreated behind my hands. Lucas shook his head. The teacher nodded, moving his attention to another table.

***

Lunchtime in Portum, the older boys are arguing over "spamming" in Super Smash Bros. Brawl. No matter where you were standing, you could hear them shouting.

Lucas encouraged me to go inside the lion's den. 'Go on, they're not gonna eat you,' he said. I trudged inside, only for him to disappear. *I really, really don't belong here.*

Dyspraxia inhibited my skill in certain genres of video games, and if you played badly, the other boys would tease you. So joining in was off the menu. I trembled, frozen in a bubble of sweat, flinching whenever they shrieked or leapt into the air.

'Hi, what's your name?' My bones rattled, I could have literally jumped out of my skin. The voice from behind me belonged to a girl, one of the mainstream peer supporters. They'd come up to Portum, volunteering their time. She tapped her feet, blinking. 'Uh, sorry. Did I—'

'My name's Max,' I spluttered. 'I'm in year seven.' She led me back to Lucas, my cheeks glowing a flushing red.

'I'm sorry, Max. I didn't know,' Lucas gulped, his vocal pitch raised. We paused, sitting together in silence for a while. 'Do you miss primary school? I'm sorry Susan isn't—'

'If I could kill that bitch I would.' Lucas's eyes gaped wide, like he'd seen a puppy transform into a flesh-ripping demon. 'I fucking hate her. If I see her, I will kill her.'

'OK. Have you played any good games recently?' he asked.

'Dad says he'll get me Game Dev Tycoon, if I do well in school.'

'I think you have been doing well. I liked the story you wrote. You deserve it.'

'Thanks.'

'So, what's the game about?'

'You run a game development company.'

'Sounds fun, is it an RPG?' (That's a role-playing game.)

'No, it's a tycoon game.'

'I see. Have you played any RPGs? Like Pokémon?'

'No.'

'It's all about strategy. You'll like it.'

***

Charlotte took me for my last lesson of the day, period five. Immediately, we were squashed together like livestock on the stairs. Teenagers called to each other at the top of their lungs, they pushed past their peers, it was every man for themselves. The subject we were headed to was called SEAL.

'Line up from tallest to shortest,' ordered the teacher. I made my way to the end of the line.

'I think I'm the shortest,' I whispered meekly.

For the first few weeks, I'd always come home with heavy legs. I didn't have much time to catch my breath in between lessons. One noisy classroom, a hellish hallway, another classroom. Rinse and repeat. I only had Lucas and Arthur to hang out with at lunchtime. The rest of my cohort seemed to settle in faster. Zach loved Nintendo, so he had no problems getting on with the older boys. Jordan never stopped smiling, always asking people if he could help them. Adrian learnt English quickly, Charlotte praised him for his efforts. Secretly, I hoped one of the mainstream students would wander into Portum and start talking to me.

New year-sevens visited Portum within their first weeks of starting at Crown Heights School. Charlotte allocated time to "teach them about autism", so that they "understood their Portum peers". They came when all the Portum pupils were out attending lessons, but I was unfortunate enough to be caught in the crossfire, watching them swarm into the kitchen like flies on an animal's carcass. Brushing aside chairs, knocking various things around in the Portum garden.

'This place is for retarded people,' one of them whispered. Charlotte stood with hands on hips, a slight smile. *Why does she think they're kind? Why?* I bolted, finding a tiny room. "Mondrian." I glanced back, finding Charlotte absorbed in calming the crowd. *Just till Lucas gets here.*

***

The Mondrian Room, barely modest in size. A table and chair at one end, a giant purple-beanbag and massage chair at the other. I peered back into the kitchen, where Charlotte was still trying to tame my rowdy mainstream peers. *Oh well, better here than in there.* From that day forward, the Mondrian Room became my base of operations. I'd rush inside the second I arrived at school.

'I'll go to Wood House for one night,' I said. Charlotte smiled, her eyes widening.

'You know that's so mature, and it's really fantastic you're coming.'

'But only for one night, got it?'

'Yes, of course. Can I do anything to make it easier for you?'

'Pizza, hot chocolate, not sleeping in a tent and a box of my dad's hair.' I crossed my arms. 'Never mind, just joking.' I held dad's hair for comfort, a tingling in my fingers demanded it. A night seemed easy enough. All I needed to do was conceal my pull-ups. Perhaps I'd make a friend.

The trip was for the year sevens, eights, and nines. The older children slept in tents. My cohort got a room with bunkbeds. Adrian often provoked and insulted me in science. So, I chose top bunk. That way if he tried anything while I was sleeping, I'd be alerted by the sound of him climbing the ladder.

With Arthur, I made immature jokes that my grandmother would regard as "horrid schoolboy humour". I spent most of the trip with him and Lucas. The older boys stayed amongst themselves, playing Super Smash Bros. *Is that all they ever do?* The Wii was basically off limits to my cohort, except for Zach; he played well enough to for the older kids to accept him.

Jordan and Adrian enjoyed the great outdoors more than I did. So, it was reading or hanging out with Arthur and Lucas. Adrian stared at me from the other bunk bed, I kept rubbing my eyes. *Don't go to sleep. Don't go to sleep.* We kept staring at each other. Who would last the longest? It was Adrian.

'I heard him talk,' Adrian said, with an enormous grin. I ran a hand across my cheek, my gaze meeting the floor.

'Oh, what was he saying?' Charlotte asked.

'He said he didn't want to go to sleep.'

***

Lucas found me lying down atop my sleeping-bag. 'Max, is everything OK?'

'I'm fine, just bored.'

He sat on the bunk bed. 'Have you read your book?'

'Read it twice.'

'Try talking to Jordan, or Adrian. They don't have anyone to speak to.'

I sat up, shaking my head. 'No point. I shouldn't have come here. It's boring.'

'You wanna watch a movie?' He brandished a VHS tape, Monsters, Inc.

'There's only one TV that plays VHS tapes. And we can't use it.'

'Why not?'

Sighing, I got up and pointed to the older boys. Their eyes fixated on the television. Fingers mashing the controllers. They chattered away loudly, with endless bravado.

'Oh, I'm sure they'll let us borrow it.'

'Nah, all they ever do is play that stupid game. They can't imagine anything else.'

'Let me try.'

'Enjoy getting sworn at.'

'Trust me, Max, I can do this for you.'

My jaw flew open when he returned with the television. With a big grin, he placed it on the floor. 'How about we share it?'

I raised an eyebrow. 'With who?'

'Zach, Adrian, Jordan. Come on, it'll be fun.'

'OK, fine.'

He and Arthur brought in the beanbags. We gathered around the television, but neither man could make it work. 'Let me try,' I offered.

Everyone watched on, mesmerised as I tinkered with the archaic machine. Finally, the screen flickered to life.

'How did you get it working?' asked Arthur.

'Switch the display to composite,' I replied.

For the next hour, we sat in silence. 'Are you having fun, Macky?' dad asked, mum in tow.

'Uh-.' My face burned up. *Did he have to say Macky?*

73

'Are you Max's dad?' Jordan asked, beaming.

'Yes, I'm his dad. This is his mum. We're here to take him home.'

'Dad, let's just go.' I led them by the hand, dodging everyone.

'Hey, are you Max's dad?' One of the older boys asked. *Shit.*

'Yes, we're Max's parents.'

'Why is Max so small?' he questioned. My heart fell limp, then jolted to life.

'It runs in the family. Max will grow,' dad replied.

I pulled both embarrassing parents to the car after that. When I returned to school the next day all my lessons awaited, Music, Textiles, English, Maths, History, and countless other subjects. Running through narrow hallways, dodging teenagers, trying not to get trampled. Crucially, I had to be careful in the mornings when I was alone.

A group of boys laughing and pushing each other around? I always ran the other way, not worth the risk. The stairs? Don't stop, keep running. So why didn't I use the empty hallways, the ones with fewer students around? Fewer students meant fewer staff. If one bad agitator caught me alone, God only knows what would transpire.

On particularly busy days, I took the risk. I always checked twice behind me, then in front. One wrong step and I'd be in for years of bullying. Every transition involving the stairs left me panting, shaking, and dripping with sweat. *How many more times do I have to do this? Probably a thousand at least.* I spent lessons living in fear, avoiding the gaze of my peers. Classes were "boring". Why would I ever go to music to sing about smelly socks?

'Lucas, please tell me what I'm learning here.' Why read the same book in English fifteen lessons in a row. Why suffer in textiles? With my motor skills, the fabrics were impossible to line up. In ICT, we only seemed to talk about E-Safety. What was the purpose of it all? My schoolbag filled to the brim with books and stationery. A never-ending tale of boisterous teenagers and infinite subjects.

Why bother with one essay when another comes along a second later? No end in sight, I couldn't see the road of academia leading anywhere. Thankfully, Charlotte listened to me about PE. *Maybe I can drop other subjects too.* In Portum, we slaved away doing piles of homework. But we had "social skills" too, hosted by Charlotte in the Big Room.

My cohort of year sevens, and a year eleven named Roy who I knew from my bus. *He's not even in year seven, why's he here?* Her lectures involved "touching people on the shoulder" and "being kind". *Tell that to the ones playing Super Smash Bros..* Whenever I gave my opinion, Charlotte would say I was "so insightful". Jordan spent most of the lesson smiling and talking about how much he disliked the school's various noises.

Adrian and Zach had needed prompts to engage in the lesson. As for Roy, he always brought up how he was "older than us". Despite numerous Portum staff prompting me, I refused to go to the school canteen. It smelled like liquefied garbage, to communicate people shouted over each other, and on one occasion a Portum student was targeted and had his tray knocked to the floor.

I walked in there only once and thankfully never again. Rather than having school lunch or packed lunch, a TA would take me out to get my food from the local high street at lunchtime. My meal was always a milkshake from the park café and chicken from the local fast-food joint. By Christmas, I wore a coat and hoodie to school, and for that matter to just about everywhere else, except at home or in my grandparents' flat. Rain or sweltering sunshine, I always concealed my face. It was an odd fashion choice that attracted strange looks, but I didn't have to see them. In fact, I never had to make eye contact with anyone.

I depended on my coat and hoodie for a sense of safety in what I perceived to be an unforgiving school. It also softened the blow when people bumped into me on the stairs. Nobody could convince me to take it off, not even grandma.

Chapter 8: Galactic Conquest

Adrian cackled, kicking open the door. My heart was flung into my ribcage and we were soon wrestling for my laptop. After being punched in the face, he retreated. I gave chase, wielding a compass as my weapon. 'Get back here, motherfucker.'

He stuck his tongue out before tripping on the steps. I pounced, stabbing him in the back. A shriek of pain thundered through Portum. Charlotte rushed out, finding Adrian staggering to his feet and jolting away.

'And don't come back you bastard.' I yelled, grinning as he screamed.

'What do you think you're doing?' Charlotte shouted.

'Um...'

'Give it to me. Please.' With a twitching, sweat-stricken hand I gave her the compass. 'Thank you, now I'd really appreciate it if...' I stormed off back to the Mondrian Room, slamming the door. Charlotte followed me in there.

'You're lucky it was plastic. You might have broken his spine.'

'Really? In that case, I should have used a metal one.'

'I know you don't want to hurt people.'

'This scratch on my laptop? He fucking did it.' I held up my laptop, dragging a finger across the slightly damaged casing.

'I'm very sorry about that but—'

'I've been leaving him alone. Then he comes in here and spoils my YouTube video.'

'You know, your parents bought you a laptop for schoolwork, not to watch YouTube videos.'

'Are you taking his side? He came into my room and ruined shit.'

'It's not your room, it's the Mondrian Room. And everyone in Portum can use it.' I turned on my laptop, ignoring her. 'If you're not gonna say anything useful, then leave.'

'No, I won't leave. You're very angry, and it's important we're all kind to each other in Portum.'

I groaned. *Yeah, because trying to steal my laptop is kind.* 'Does Adrian have to be kind?'

'Yes, and you know he's made a lot of progress. He's not touching people anymore.'

'What will it take for you to fuc... leave me alone?'

'Well done for stopping yourself swearing. All I'd like you to do is apologise and read a story with me.'

'Only if it's a quick one.'

'It is, I promise you.'

'Adrian better apologise too.'

78

'I'm sure he'll apologise. Give me a moment.'

She returned, a book in hand. I raised an eyebrow. *'Angry Arthur?'*

'I think you'll find it helpful.' She read it. I peered from behind my computer. 'Did his anger solve anything?'

'He destroyed the world.'

'Yes, but did he get what he wanted?'

I shook my head. 'Are you trying to say I didn't get what I wanted? Because I did. I hurt Adrian.'

'Is that what you wanted?'

'I wanted him to leave me alone. But he doesn't listen.'

'Will he listen now that you've hurt him?'

I ended up apologising to a shaken Adrian, who never bothered me again. Instead, he annoyed other students, particularly the older boys in the middle of their Super Smash Bros. tournaments.

***

When Charlotte told me that Portum students aren't forced to attend lessons, I dropped every subject.

I spent all my time in the Mondrian Room. I didn't have any friends, so Lucas and Arthur became my company. We'd play Monopoly, Pokémon, Minecraft. I spent a lot of time writing stories. Nobody could persuade me to go to lessons, nobody could persuade me to remove my hood. *Why bother in school?* was the view I took. Lessons were a barrage of boisterous chatter and never-ending work. Everywhere I set foot, teenagers rampaged, pushing each other, almost knocking me over. If this was education, I wanted absolutely no part in it.

Out of a longing for chocolate milk, the same brand they served in the canteen at primary school, I tracked down the wholesaler in Germany, convincing them to give me fifteen free cartons.

***

'Max, can I just say how clever you are? This is fantastic,' Charlotte said in complimenting me. 'I'm just wondering what you'll do when you run out. Maybe we can ask Susan—'

'She's a demon,' I said with contempt.

'She was very fond of you.'

'No, she's a demon. Fuck her.'

'Sometimes people who care about you do things that upset you. Remember when I took your laptop away?'

'You apologised. That bitch thinks she's right about everything.'

'What if I emailed her and asked for an apology?' Charlotte suggested.

I paused, running a hand through my hair. 'You can try it, but she'll never listen. Like I said, she's a demon.'

***

As an unwelcome interruption one lunchtime, some of my mainstream peers rushed into the Mondrian Room.

'Why are you here?' I asked. Two girls and a boy, they'd taken up residence on the beanbag.

'Mrs. Richards told us to spend time with you or something.'

God damn it, Charlotte. I hunkered down, playing a game on my computer. *They'll get bored, eventually.* A scrunched-up ball of paper struck me.

'Is he crying?'

'You shouldn't have done that,' one of them said

Frozen, I waited for the bell. *Five more minutes. Four more minutes. Three more minutes.*

'The bell's gonna go. See ya, Max.'

Thank God. I scrutinised every corner of the room, correcting any perceived "damage". The Mondrian Room desolate once again. *Maybe I need some friends. But not those twats.* Everywhere in the real world seemed a danger zone. Why do I tremble when I talk to someone my age? How do I start a conversation without cringing?

I sought refuge in the internet, a place without eye contact. Nobody pushes you, there are no narrow corridors. It didn't take long for me to find Galactic Conquest, a MMORPG. (For the uninitiated, I'd suggest doing a bit of research. But as for my explanation, imagine a video game where you're always playing with other people online.) It had laser guns and glowing blades of all sorts.

I joined the largest guild on my server, the Devil Dogs. (Guilds are typically a collection of players who play together.) In the actual world, I was "Max", the tiny boy concealed under a hood, fearing for his safety. On Galactic Conquest, I was the mighty warrior XMA24.

I spent most of my time in the guild. We killed enemy players, defended our base, and participated in drills and regular training. If I impressed my commanders, I'd get rewarded with a promotion. However, in every training I'd have to compete with upwards of twenty comrades. Dyspraxia hindered my ability to hit a target, my reaction times were always seconds too late. I couldn't complete drills fast enough, and as a "consequence" my superiors had me do laps around the base. Every order, every battle, even if they used me as cannon fodder, I served, eventually earning the rank of sergeant and serving in a squad.

Soon I'd become my superiors, I'd have power, I could order people around. Unlike school, there was an end goal, a purpose. Thrashed in the corridors at school but a warrior online, clad in yellow and white armour, destroying the enemy with my squad mates. I'd never been a champion at getting to sleep, but Galactic Conquest was more interesting than school. I'd spend hours playing, sleeping late at night.

Every morning became a battle with dad. Every morning he carried me down the stairs, enduring whatever I threw at him; I punched, kicked and scratched him.

No matter what, he'd have me dressed, teeth cleaned, hair brushed, and onto the bus in time. The status quo became lessons sacrificed for time playing Monopoly and Pokémon in school, with sleep sacrificed for Galactic Conquest.

The commanders in the Devil Dogs continued to use my squad as cannon fodder. Of all the players, we were the least skilled, often holding impossible positions to delay the enemy. And whilst distraction and delay can be strategically sound, we couldn't help but feel left out. Rarely promoted, never recognised, we got no help if the enemy surrounded our unit.

I tried to become a commando; in a guild, the best players had that title. They dismissed me immediately, though not because of my skill level but because I didn't memorise an "oath" that no one had told me about. That's why when browsing our Enjin forums one night, I took an opportunity. A member named Draxx14 was leaving the Devil Dogs and requesting help with a guild named the Shadow Imperium. In Galactic Conquest, you're only allowed to belong to one guild at a time. If you try to steal a guild's members it's called "poaching". You're usually branded as a traitor and shot.

Sometimes, smaller guilds who want to make an example of their enemies will repeatedly hunt and kill a "poacher" until they leave the game or make a new account. In layman's terms, that's cyberbullying. A lunge at someone's self-esteem.

Fortunately for Draxx14, he'd only sacrificed his rank. But why associate with a traitor? Why would joining Draxx14 be an opportunity? First, the Devil Dogs were too big to care about him. Second, Draxx14 wasn't the leader of the Shadow Imperium. That honour belonged to Starboy23. Until I joined, it was only the two of them. Getting in on the ground floor meant I could become a "high commander", a title which I had soon earned through my dedication to the cause.

Unlike the commanders in the Devil Dogs, Draxx14 taught me how to be better at the game. I realised my slow reaction times would even out if I used faster weapons: a mini-gun to douse my enemies with laser-bolts; and a Katana to finish them off quickly at close range. It was just the three of us, desperately trying to recruit players. Starboy23 had angered the leader of another guild, so we were always being hunted. Base after base we built ended up being destroyed within a day. But through sheer grit over many months, we built the Shadow Imperium from nothing, growing to 300 members by July. Draxx14 and I led an assault against the guild who were hunting us. Fighting side by side, we burned their base to the ground. Through victory, we created the foundation of an empire.

The troops assigned to me became my close friends, Bradford943, Vish09, the list goes on. I'd found refuge, an escape from all the screaming in the school corridors. A place where I had power and people respected me, where I wasn't just a little boy cowering behind a hood.

Year seven was over. I hadn't a single friend in school and refused to attend any lessons. I spent most of my days in the Mondrian Room with Lucas and Arthur – not that they were poor company. Summer brought more time for Galactic Conquest. But trouble was brewing in the Shadow Imperium. Starboy23 had married another player in-game. (Not a real wedding, obviously. Some preferred the role-play aspect of the game to bloodshed.)

The Shadow Imperium was an empire, and the primary purpose of our guild was to wage war. Thus, introducing a family and having a marriage wasn't popular. Despite minor protests, the wedding proceeded. I stood on a balcony next to Draxx14. Below us were the lower-ranked members. If they came too near, they'd get shot.

Personally, I was sceptical. Our leader starting a family and having a wedding in a war guild? As for his bride, "Jessica14", why was she deserving of power? Starboy23 had only met her last week. Everyone on that balcony except her had earned their rank. Yet she was in charge of us? Out of respect for Starboy23 and Draxx14, I didn't complain.

Jessica14 emerged, striding close to Starboy23.

A speech bubble appeared on the screen. «I don't like this dress.»

We all had to wait for her to change.

Then the ceremony proceeded without hiccups. They chose members of the guild to be "sons" and "uncles", answerable only to Starboy23 and Jessica14. Effectively, we now had an aristocracy. (Yes, I know I'm writing about teenagers playing an online game, but we all took it very seriously.) Within hours, there were dozens of complaints about the new command structure.

23.7.14

(A private message from one of my men.)

We must stop Jessica. She is ruining the Shadow Imperium. We can't allow her to ruin everything. You, Draxx and Starboy have done for this guild. Starboy doesn't see this, but I know you do.

***

«Greetings, Mistress Jessica.» one of my men said.

«STFU, bitch, I fucking hate you,» she replied.

None of my fellow commanders did anything, so I went to Draxx14. (Starboy23 was on "vacation".)

«Calm down. Wait here till I sort it,» Draxx14 said.

A jail cell? I have done nothing wrong.

«Why in here?»

«I don't want people getting suspicious. Might think we're planning a coup.»

«OK.» I went inside, allowing him to raise the forcefield. Despite having ample opportunity to speak to

Jessica14 and address the issue, he never did. Whilst Jessica14 went about abusing her power and I languished in my cell, he invited one of his old commanding officers from the Devil Dogs, Diablous034, to our base.

At first I thought the new arrival was here to help resolve things, but he ignored anyone "unworthy of his respect". Half an hour later, I couldn't bear it anymore. I messaged Insanekiller200, an officer who was Jessica14's "son". We were close friends, and because he was part of the aristocracy, the guards couldn't stop him from freeing me. Making sure we weren't being followed, we ventured outside of Shadow Imperium territory. Something had to be done about Jessica14.

***

«Thanks,» I said.

«No problem, it's stupid how the guards can't take orders from you.»

«I hate it when they shoot people for getting too close. But we have bigger problems. Has Draxx done anything about Jessica?»

«Nope, but he's letting Diablous boss us around.»

«Let's deal with Jessica first. The Shadow Imperium isn't strong enough to fight the Devil Dogs.»

«She should get exiled. I'm only her "son" because I respect Starboy.»

«We'll talk to her first. She might change her ways.»

«I'll get her to come here. But she won't change, she just wants power.» He messaged her and we waited.

***

«This better be good,» Jessica14 grumbled. I prepared to draw my weapon, just in case.

«You need to stop abusing people,» Insanekiller200 demanded. She pointed a sword at me.

«Has XMA brainwashed you?»

«Will you change your ways?» I asked, drawing my Katana.

«You can't take my kids away from me.»

«I'm not your son,» Insanekiller200 retorted.

«Starboy23 will exile you for this, XMA.»

«Jessica, I promised to protect my men. I plan on keeping it, and I won't let you bully them.»

«When Starboy23 gets back, you're dead.»

«I won't let someone like you bully my men. I will fight you till the end, Jessica.»

«I will make sure everythink you care about is gone.»

«If you're gonna threaten him, at least spell correctly.»

She left, spouting more threats with rather terrible spelling.

«Told you so, XMA.»

«We will rebel; we'll call ourselves the Paladins.» A fateful decision. Why did I make it? We'd already risked our ranks and made a powerful enemy. The way I saw it, nobody else would act against Jessica14. Like Susan, she seemed an invulnerable obstacle. My happiness threatened, my troops under threat. I wasn't about to let history repeat itself.

Chapter 9: Power

«I watched your video. I hate fucking rebels,» a guard boomed. Four of them encircled us, weapons drawn. We were the Paladins, protesting against Jessica14's tyranny.

«We're not your enemies,» I appealed. «Can't you see Jessica is using you?»

«Paladin fucks. I don't care.»

«You should, we're your brothers.»

«I will not betray the Imperium.»

I stepped forward. «We're fighting for you, our brothers.»

«Back up now. All of you.»

«Sir?» a Paladin asked. I had sent a message to my fellows, a private one only they could see.

«Let them shoot first, I'm recording.»

Surrounded, weapons ready, we stood still. My hands shook, sweat trickling onto the mouse. «What now?»

«You're all under arrest.»

A Paladin trudged forward. «You can't arrest us for wanting freedom.» The guards unloaded a fierce torrent of laser fire into his skull.

«Attack!» I ordered. We opened fire. Adrenaline coursed through my veins; the thunder of laser fire consumed all else. Everything on screen flared an invasive blue. You couldn't tell which gun the blasts came from. Heavily injured and down two men, we miraculously survived.

«They'll bring backup. Take the balcony!»

«Yes, sir.»

My mini gun gave us an advantage at close range. From a high vantage point, an otherwise short firefight would become a lengthy standoff. My breaths raw and uneasy, we waited. One of us peered out, falling victim to a well-placed sniper. If either side pressed an offensive, they'd fall victim to concentrated laser fire.

The men who had respawned were already fighting in their own pockets. (You have limitless "lives" on Galactic Conquest.) But our primary force held the balcony, home to Jessica14's aristocracy. Who would break first? What did it say if the Paladins, a group many referred to as "bandits", could hold the balcony hostage?

A long game of snipers followed until finally Draxx14 arrived. «Everyone stand down,» he ordered. We lowered our weapons, meeting him outside in shoulder to shoulder formation.

«I have the full video, they shot first,» I said. Draxx14 and Diablous034 scrutinised both parties, checking their weapons, kill counts and deaths.

«I'll watch the video, but you should have waited. Now we're at risk of civil war.»

«Just get rid of the family.»

«I agree with you, but that's up to Starboy23.»

«When's he coming back?»

«Tomorrow. You may recruit supporters, if you wish.»

«Thank you.»

«But if I learn of any more attacks, I'm going to exile you all. If you try to come back after that, I'll shoot you myself.»

«This is bullshit,» a Paladin said.

«Remember, we're not trying to destroy the Imperium,» I replied.

«Draxx, I want to speak with you in private,» Diablous034 requested.

«I'll be back. Dismissed.»

Some joined us, mostly my men and our less-skilled players. Others sympathised but didn't want to risk their ranks. Then you had the hardliners, people who called us "traitors" and "bandits". They wanted to prove our intentions were the "destruction of the Shadow Imperium".

We held firm for weeks, never wavered, never fell for provocations. We had a theme song we used in our propaganda, "Knights of Cydonia" by Muse. Insanekiller200 introduced me to a band called Disturbed. Thus, a new tradition was born; I had a playlist on Spotify. Music would accompany me into battle.

Disturbed became my favourite band and still is to this day. Appropriately, "Warrior" was the first song I ever heard by them. The lyrics, the drums, the guitar solo – I'd heard nothing so riveting, so adrenaline pumping, so energetic. But Disturbed was just a gateway drug, later I would go on to discover Breaking Benjamin, Dream Evil, Avenged Sevenfold and many more.

I'd found a sound I identified with, a piece of my identity in emerging adolescence. Something that separated me from the Smash Bros. clique at Portum. Adults told me, "Video games rot your brain."; "It's all a bunch of noise." What did they know? I'd found empowerment, a place where I was happy.

In real life, I couldn't take "revenge" on Susan or stop the pushing and shoving on the stairs at school. In Galactic Conquest, my enemies fell. I typed Jessica14's name into Google and found his YouTube channel. Like me, he was an eleven-year-old boy. Unlike me, he had lied about his identity. I sent a video of him singing One Direction songs to Starboy23. Within a day he'd been evicted from the Shadow Imperium. Subsequently, his YouTube channel was flooded with dislikes and venomous comments. An early birthday present, I'd return to school revelling in my newfound power.

27.8.14

Dear Parents,

Several of you know, I think. But I wanted to make sure that all our parents and students know that our headmaster, Alfie, died over the bank holiday weekend. He had been unwell and was unable to attend school last term. Tragically, he took his own life on Sunday.

It is because of Alfie that Portum is here, and his passion for, and commitment to, inclusion and his support for Portum has been total. I cannot imagine Portum and Crown Heights School without his energy and enthusiasm and love. Our students have had different levels, types of interactions and contact with Alfie. He spent a lot of time up here, talking with us and eating our bananas!

Please can you talk to your sons about it so they are prepared, when they return to school, for the sadness and the tributes and memorial services they will encounter. I hope your summer break has been good. I'm pleased to tell you all that our Year 11 boys did really well in their GCSEs – so proud of them!

With good wishes,
Charlotte

Everyone missed "Alf". They erected a memorial swing in the Portum garden. Students had built a shrine to him at the entrance. He had waved at me a few times, said hello with a bright smile. But he was just a face in a school I perceived as dangerous. Everyone talked about him while I still sought shelter under my hood.

Armed with the iPod Nano I'd got for my birthday, I went on the bus each morning. Music helped with the journey, it was the lull between rushes on the stairs and preparation for battles in Galactic Conquest. I tried to attend lessons; I thought my experience online would help me academically. In fact, I never faltered on subjects where I could type an essay. History, Religious Education, English. But Mathematics? What's the point of knowing the letter b equals five? Languages? I only chose Spanish because it had the least homework and because it was closest to the exit corridor.

With some coaxing from Charlotte and Lucas, I made my first friend, Jayden, one of the new year sevens at Portum. We shared a bus and a lot of the same humour.

'It's lovely to see them chatting,' our escort told my parents. The older boys glared, telling us to be quiet. *You never shut up about Smash Bros.* The words were in my head, but they never left my mouth. With my own fragility in mind, I couldn't risk provoking anyone.

They had introduced me to a TA, Oliver. He took me to lessons or to get my lunch when Lucas and Arthur weren't available. I swore at him a lot, hardly spoke to him. *He has to earn my respect.* Oliver had done nothing wrong, but Susan had left me hollow. I found it difficult to trust another TA.

95

Egotism played a role too. My newfound power online affected who I perceived as an equal.

***

'Miss is strict. Might want to take your coat off,' Oliver suggested. I ignored him, opening the classroom door.

'Listen,' the teacher boomed. Oliver and I took our seats, her eyes pursuing us. 'Take it off, now.' Her voice spewed sharp needles. I pulled my hood closer, concealing more of my face.

'Well?'

No, fuck you! No, fuck you! Why can't I say it? She knelt down to my eye level, her breath brushing against my face.

I turned to Oliver, his facial expression unmoving. 'Max, let's go,' he whispered.

Fuck you, I'm not taking it off. I'm leader of the Paladins, High Commander in the Shadow Imperium. Why can't... I gave a sheepish nod, leaving with Oliver.

'See, I will not tolerate disrespect in my classroom,' the teacher called, jabbing a finger at us. My face fizzed with heat. *Disrespect.* I peered at Oliver. *I've been an asshole...*

'I'm sorry, Max,' he lamented.

'For what? It's my fault. I'm sorry for being such an asshole.' Rain battered us on the way out.

'Apology accepted. At least you're safe from the rain.'

'Yeah, I guess.' We plodded through the playground, back into the building Portum was in.

'I don't think she realised—'

'She did, you were with me. But people like her don't give a crap.'

'I can have Charlotte talk to her for next time.'

'I'm not going back. And again, I'm sorry for being an asshole. I don't wanna end up like her.'

***

Boisterous laughter, screaming, everyone shoving each other. Crammed onto a tiny staircase, I'd lost sight of Lucas. *Oh shit, oh shit! Run!* Two behemoths blocked my path, I couldn't escape. We funnelled out slower than rush-hour traffic on the North Circular.

Shoved to the ground, forehead smashing into the cruel mud-covered floor. I squeezed my throat, repelling the tears. Almost trampled, I rolled away from the stampede, limping outside.

'Max, are you OK?' Lucas asked.

'I... I'm fine.' A haunting void dominated my chest, squeezing tightly with every wounded step to the bus. *Hold it in.* I sat down next to Jayden; head bowed.

'Max, I think Adrian shouted rape in the corridor.' He laughed. No response, not even a chuckle. 'Are you alright?'

'I... I.' My eyes detonated a flood of tears.

97

'What happened to him?' one of the older boys asked.

'You can tell us, honey. What's wrong?' the escort asked.

'Someone from my old school attacked me with a knife. I'm gonna kill their family.'

'Max is drunk,' Roy blurted out.

'Shut the fuck up, Roy. Or I'll stick a compass up your fucking ass,' I yelled.

'You're drunk.'

'I'll shoot your dad, you fat fuck.' He fumbled with his seatbelt. Luckily, we were driving.

'He's just upset, Roy, he doesn't mean it,' the escort consoled.

But I stomped on his foot when leaving the bus, darting through the door, sobbing hysterically. The outstanding leader of the Paladins humbled, weeping into his mother's clothes.

***

'Max, stop, you don't need a knife,' mum beseeched me.

'I do, or they'll kill me.'

'No one is going to kill you.' She wrested the knife from my hands, preventing me from bringing it to school the next day.

***

'Max, you don't have to go to Spanish anymore but—' Charlotte said, only to be interrupted.

'I'm not going to lessons today either.'

'And that's fine, we can't force you to do anything. But your mother told me you wanted to bring a knife into school. And that's not OK.'

'I need it.'

'No, you don't. You're safe at Portum, you don't need a weapon.' *Bullshit.* 'And you know, it's an offence to carry a knife.'

But without a weapon, what chance did I stand? The only place I could stand up for myself was Galactic Conquest. I had dominated Jessica14. If ever he logged in, I'd be one of the first ones to try and kill him.

An expression of power and the sole place of empowerment. Yet even there things were changing. Draxx14 chose random people to become high-ranking officers, favouring them over members who had proved themselves and their loyalty. For representation, they came to me.

***

«It's unfair though,» I protested. «Most of them have been loyal for months.»

«I trust them,» Draxx14 replied.

«It's his decision. Know your place, XMA,» Diablous034 added.

«You're not even in the Shadow Imperium. Don't give me that crap.»

«Need I remind you they passed leadership of the Devil Dogs onto myself and Invicta11?»

«Your leader left to join the army; doesn't mean you can boss us around.»

«Draxx, demote him.»

«For freedom of speech? Draxx isn't corrupt like you.»

«XMA, stop, or I will demote you.»

«But I've been loyal since the start.»

«Demoted,» Draxx14 declared. Now I was only a rank above being a non-commissioned officer. My heart fell, the horrible void returned. «You might wanna leave. We have things to discuss.»

Soon I and my fellow officers got called back, Draxx14 and Diablous034 had made an important decision. Because Starboy23 was busy with high school, Draxx14 would take ownership of the guild. Given Starboy23's misstep with the marriage and his inactivity, it made sense. He'd succeed more as a commander. I supported the idea, but suggested the lower ranks vote for who they wanted as leader. The other high ranks overwhelmingly rejected my proposal, and everyone bickered amongst themselves.

«This is a power grab,» I said.

«No it isn't, Starboy is just incompetent.»

Many flocked to Draxx14, many saw him as the one who built the Shadow Imperium.

«We'll settle this with a practice raid,» Draxx14 ordered.

There were two teams, Draxx14's and Starboy23's. Whoever won would have leadership of the Imperium. Naturally, the most skilled players got chosen by Draxx14; everyone else, including me, was on Starboy23's team. Against a superior foe, we had to achieve the most kills within half an hour. Fingers trembling on the mouse, sweat and adrenaline mixing into an inexplicable brew. I turned on my playlist. "Indestructible" by Disturbed was up first.

'Turn it down,' mum called. I took cover behind a crate.

'Can't, I need to hear who's shooting me.'

'If you concentrated like this in school.' Her voice was drowned out by the sound of laser fire.

«Fall back,» I ordered. A commando pursued us, leaping from cover to cover. Every laser blast from my weapon was expertly dodged. A grenade, a roaring explosion. I'm dead.

«We're completely fucked,» Starboy23 called. Huddled in an abandoned warehouse, enemies closing in, my music clashed with laser fire, grenades, the clashing of blades. The sweat was unrelenting, the adrenaline overflowing. Stabbed, blown up, killed and tea-bagged. But like the men of Osowiec Fortress, we fought on.

With a swift slash through the torso, I killed an enemy.

«Oi, XMA, one on one, mate,» enticed Draxx14.

«Sure.»

A dance of blades, katana against the broadsword. Parry, dodge, both of us trying to outmanoeuvre the other. I lunge and suddenly I'm dead. I didn't even see it. Draxx14 felled me with a cruel stab to the chest. Their forces overwhelmed us, Draxx14 had won the day. I rested my head against the desk.

Draxx14 gave his inauguration speech. But I couldn't watch it without suffering a desolate void of pain. I paced around my room. *It's not fair. If I hadn't been born with this bullshit I'd have won.* A stray tear slid down my face. 'Look at me, talking to myself. I'm insane,' I said aloud. *I just want a normal life. Average height, some friends, no bloody autism.* 'Is that too much to ask?'

Behind a veil of self-loathing, I desired control in a seemingly unforgiving world. Or perhaps I wanted what all humans secretly and sometimes unknowingly covet. Power.

Chapter 10: Desire

January 3rd, 2015, two weeks after Draxx14's coup. I left the Shadow Imperium and some of my men followed. We made the Paladins an official guild, independent of the Shadow Imperium. Albeit that it was more of a gang than an organised army.

«You don't have to be as good as Draxx,» Bradford943 reassured me. «I still respect you.»

«If I don't practice,» I said, brandishing my katana, «I'll never get better.»

«Fair enough.» He drew his weapon. «Are you sure about making me second-in-command though?»

«Insanekiller hasn't logged in for months. You're the only person I can trust to replace him.»

We practised every day, all of us. I insisted on it, not wanting to undergo another humiliation. Out of goodwill and friendship, we helped Draxx14 and the Shadow Imperium with the odd battle here and there. My endgame was to become one of the most revered players in the game; to gain real power, an achievement I'd be proud of. Something worth living for. Finally, I had discovered one of my talents, gaining followers, rallying people to a cause. Leadership. I believed expanding upon it would make me more than a defenceless child cowering under a hood.

Compared to me, everyone in Portum was gigantic, especially my fellow pupils.

'Are-are you putting drugs in his milkshake?' Roy stuttered.

I gritted my teeth, imagining throwing Roy's face into a woodchipper. In my head, mum's voice echoed, *Oh, but Max, he has learning difficulties.* Then my own: *Fuck his stutter and fuck him!* The way I saw it, Portum pupils were just as "dangerous" to my safety. Mum often told me Roy had "learning difficulties". It didn't matter; except for Jayden they were all potential threats. It's why I seldom used the Portum toilets, if at all.

'No, it's for his weight,' Oliver replied.

The shortest, scrawniest pupil in Portum, an invisible title that came with unwanted remarks. Everyone else "belonged there", but I was an apple in a banana patch. Small, terrible at Super Smash Bros., only friends with one year seven. All my days were spent in the Mondrian Room, occasionally going to a lesson if the staff persuaded me.

I played games on my laptop, listened to Disturbed and Breaking Benjamin. In a school full of perceived dangers, the Mondrian Room was my sanctuary. But I recognised Portum was a sanctuary to others. *Better off here than in mainstream.* Students like Roy wouldn't last long in a crowd of year elevens. Portum gave those like him and me a chance.

When the school denied Portum the ability to fundraise via cake sales, many showed concern.

'Will Portum close?' and 'Are we gonna be downstairs with SEN?' was the gist of our anxious questions.

'We're all fine, everything is fine. There's no danger of Portum closing,' Charlotte told us. I can't possibly speak for every pupil in Portum, but I'd like to believe that most of us were consciously aware of our reliance on it. Mainstream wasn't a kind environment, and the SEN pupils who didn't meet the criteria for Portum often came to harass us at lunchtime. It wasn't just teasing and the occasional scuffle. In one incident Jayden had his Yu-Gi-Oh! cards stolen. You see, whilst some SEN pupils from the school's other provision were nice to be around, and even shared similarities with us in Portum. We had our little part of the school, and not everyone appreciated their intrusions.

12.2.15

Hello Baba and Grandma. I just want to tell you I got into the Platinum Band at school. It's the highest band (grade) you can get. The other year 8s who got in are going on a bowling trip. But for my reward, Charlotte gave me a steam voucher instead.

I'd got an A* on my Religious Education mock. It was a team effort between me and Lucas. He convinced me to take the exam and somehow scribed the entire essay before my laptop ran out of power.

'I'll buy you a milkshake for lunch, my treat,' he said.

Charlotte pushed for me to return to more classes. 'You're so clever, you can do it.'

I never read my school reports. *I'll just cheat on my GCSEs*, I thought. I'd abandoned all care for academia. Class tormented me. 'Get a job, go to university.' They told me that was the end goal. 'You're wasting your brain.' On what exactly? They weren't the ones suffering infinite essays on subjects I saw no purpose in.

In hindsight, if I'd found learning more enjoyable, I would have attended all my classes. I wanted to enjoy it, and that desire was the only reason I hadn't given up completely. I had a glimmer of hope that a lesson would interest me. Maybe one day my rowdy classmates and the torturous hallways wouldn't invoke terror.

The email to my grandparents is proof of pride, but undergoing years of what I deemed "pointless work" was far less attractive than Galactic Conquest. Power, control, friendship, all my desires were found online. And there weren't any boisterous obstacles in my way.

***

'Max, someone from White Mountain wants to see you,' Charlotte said. I buried myself in my laptop.

'I don't know you and I don't want to know you.' Charlotte led the woman away, but it turned out she was the headmistress. I believed her responsible for my suffering as she hadn't taken action against Susan. I'd been out of primary school for almost two years by that point, but I still suffered nightmares. Susan, Karen, Zoe – I'd dream of them hurting me, restraining me, vilifying me. One detail stands out: I was aware of Susan's presence in all the various dreams, heard her voice, but never saw her physically, she remained a phantom. Part of me wanted to confront her and take revenge. Yet I exploded with anxiety if someone suggested she was anywhere near me.

The song "Stricken" by Disturbed echoed my anger and fear of her. The music awakened memories of struggling against her. That song holds the first lyrics I ever related to. She hurt me and got away with it. Was she hurting other children? Those were the worst thoughts, the worst visions.

I fantasised about defeating her, like I would an enemy on Galactic Conquest. The one place I had some measure of control. But one night, outnumbered three to one, the Paladins fought against a larger guild. We fell, one by one. Bradford943 and I parried. We cut down a few until they overwhelmed us and took the capture point.

Our base, our hard work, it was theirs.

'Max, its ten o'clock at night. Go to bed,' mum called, standing in the doorway with her arms crossed.

My eyes got flooded with hot, shameful tears. 'Fuck off!'

All the messages the enemy sent us were horrible.

«Trash guild!»

«Lol, you suck!»

«My grandma can do better than these faggots.»

They took everything. Unable to fight a guild at their strength, they destroyed our hard work. There was nothing I could do, powerless in my haven.

'How dare you talk to your mother like that,' dad bellowed. A blur of tears, screaming, mum crying.

'Everything is pointless. I should just die now,' I cried. Mum couldn't download a program to save her life. Dad didn't understand the difference between online and offline. How would they ever grasp the magnitude of what I had lost? Besides, it's "silly" to have an outburst over a game.

I pretended I didn't remember my actions, that my brain had repressed it. I believe it was an excuse for my subconscious thoughts to rise. The fear of losing control, losing my purpose, became real.

***

'How was your weekend?' Charlotte asked.
'Shit.'

'I'm so sorry to hear that, would you like to talk about it?

'No.' I opened Skype, messaging Bradford943.

'Oh, are you playing a game?'

'Please leave.'

'OK then, but to me you seem very upset, so call me when you're ready to talk about it.'

I waited until she left, before sending another message. «Charlotte just left, carry on,» I said.

«We can't afford a new base yet,» Bradford943 announced. «But maybe we can if you sell some of the weapons you made.»

A message from Draxx14, I switched over to him. «Hey mate, heard what happened. I can't give you your ranks back, but I think you and the Paladins should re-join the Shadow Imperium.»

«Sorry, we won't join back. Can you give us a bit of money for a base? I'll pay you back, we'll help in battles.»

«XMA, you tried to own a guild and failed. Because you're not a true leader.» *So unfair.* «I offered you a place in the Shadow Imperium. I might have been able to give you your rank back. But here you are, begging for money, I thought you were a friend, I shouldn't even need to ask you to help in a battle.»

«I can't help you if I don't have a guild base.»

«You're being a selfish shit, don't waste more of my time. Message me if you ACTUALLY want to do something USEFUL.» The capitalisation, he always capitalised when he was serious. *What have I done to piss him off? It's not my fault...*

«Bradford, Draxx just sent me this.» Attached was a screenshot of the conversation we'd just had.

«Fuck him,» Bradford943 replied. «I ain't going back, and neither is anyone else.»

«He might have a point though. We're not strong enough.»

«Don't give me that bullshit. When I get home from school, we're rebuilding the Paladins.»

«We'll try to.»

«No, we will.»

Lucas entered the room.

«OK, thanks. See you later.» I closed down Skype.

'Max is everything alright? You look—'

'I'm fine, do we have to go to another boring lesson?'

'Uh, no, it's lunchtime.'

'Oh.'

'Are you sure you're alright, you look distant.'

'I'm fine, seriously. Let's just go.'

Bradford943 came home from school early, risking detention to help me. We didn't rebuild all we'd had overnight, but eventually we had a discreet base, out of the way of the prying eyes of larger guilds. I learnt that my end goal wasn't easy, there would be pitfalls. So I trained harder, got better at the game. Thus it consumed more of my life.

But no matter how many more members joined, no matter how many people respected me, I still lived in pain. I called my grandparents one night, telling them we were going to "attack White Mountain school" with water pistols. I wanted to put something else in the water pistol, take aim at Susan and squirt something harmful into her eyes. Dad caught me googling how to make pepper-spray on the internet. 'If I hurt her, I'll stop having nightmares about her,' I told him, after being discovered.

My trauma got worse when I learnt that Susan herself had entered Portum. Lucas and Arthur prevented her from seeing me, keeping her away from the Mondrian Room. She "understood" and "was respectful".

I thanked them repeatedly, knowing deep down that an encounter with Susan would be disastrous. I'd either freeze with fear or destroy my life in a violent outburst. Subconsciously I saw it, but I couldn't stop the visions of hurting her overwhelming my mind.

***

The Mondrian Room door repeatedly smashed open and shut, my drink plummeted to the floor. I peered up to find the perpetrator. One of the older boys, a member of the Smash Bros. clique. The noise fought against the sound of my music; the lyrics compelled me to stand up to him. Yet my quaking legs forced me into a state of submissive shock.

'Stop,' Charlotte called.

'Turn that bloody music off,' The boy shouted, kicking over a nearby bin.

'Wanker,' I muttered, turning the music up.

'It's too damn loud,' he screamed. I grinned. *Guess he's not a Disturbed fan. Shame.*

'You'll do better on the next mock. We'll help you,' Charlotte offered him by way of consolation.

'No, I failed. I failed,' He bolted to his clique, presumably burying himself in Super Smash Bros.

'Sorry, Max, he's feeling upset. I'm sure you can understand why some people find exams stressful.'

'Uh, it's fine. I'm fine.'

'Right, OK then. Let me know if you need anything.'

'Thanks,' I closed the door. Water still dampened the carpet. *Maybe I should get a paper towel.*

The older boys based themselves next door to the Mondrian Room. You could always overhear the banter and the shouting. *Never mind, I'll get Lucas to do it.* I had some awareness of emotional fragility. If I went outside even to get a paper towel, I risked being exposed to a situation that would trigger immense anxiety. In the past, volatile emotions had led to dangerous actions. Like feeling the need to "protect myself" with a weapon.

I didn't stay in the Mondrian room to get out of lessons and spend my time on recreation. It was the only place in school I could control; it served as a sanctuary and prevented my emotional immaturity from landing me in dangerous situations. Things weren't much different at home. I spent all my time playing Galactic Conquest in my bedroom.

I ate my meals there and only came out to use the toilet or take a bath. In primary school, staff forced me to be in a room by myself. Throughout adolescence, I opted for solitary occupancy of rooms just to feel safe. Unconsciously learnt behaviour perhaps? I'm not a psychiatrist, I couldn't tell you.

Whilst most teenagers "hung out with mates" for most of summer, I stayed indoors playing Galactic Conquest. Disturbed had returned from hiatus with a new album. Breaking Benjamin also brought out new music. Until that point, I'd only ventured into a few songs. Now I had a lot to expand my taste. They say the teenage years are where you "invent yourself". The music I listened to had angsty vocals and aggressive, crunchy guitar playing that expressed my emotional identity. Galactic Conquest gave me power, a "purpose". Both were the building blocks of my identity.

***

«Give me tribute,» Master Conqueror, a rival guild leader demanded. «Or we'll crush you.» Brave words and a bold name. Our guilds were around the same strength and thus equally matched opponents.

113

«You know I can't do that. Don't go to war over this.»

«Too late, XMA.» He struck me with his sword. I parried, countering with a stab to the chest. His corpse fell at my feet.

«Big mistake, cunt.» I had a plan, find his enemies, make an alliance with them. And draw Master Conqueror into an unwinnable battle.

Chapter 11: Vulnerability

"Immortalised" by Disturbed thundered out of my speakers. Laser fire shook the gorge, Master Conqueror's men fell against a mighty barrage from our lines.

«They're taking cover, sir,» a Paladin observed.

«That's what XMA wants,» Bradford943 added. I stood upon the bluff, lining up my crosshair with Master Conqueror's head. The adrenaline-filled shot connected with the target, killing him.

«The fuck. Are you cheating?» he accused.

«Jump!» I ordered, drawing my katana. Two Paladins and I jumped from the top of the canyon. Taken by surprise, Master Conqueror's men got slaughtered like sheep. The ones fast enough to run fell to an onslaught of laser fire from our primary force. Our enemies routed, demoralised, and caught in a pincer movement, we pressed the attack.

«Fuck you,» Master Conqueror screamed. «I'll tear your fucking eyes out and kill your fucking family.»

Oh, really? I grinned.

«Pathetic twat,» Bradford943 said with withering scorn.

«Surrender!» I demanded. Surrounded, his men lay down their arms.

«What the actual fuck! I didn't order you to surrender,» he screamed.

«We've lost,» one of his men said. «I'm not gonna waste my time.»

«I'll pay you ten thousand credits more,» he beseeched them.

«Lol, no.»

«You pay them?» I asked. «Pathetic.»

«You're fucking dead, XMA,»

«Nope, I have all your enemies attacking your base now.»

«They can't take the capture point if we're not there. Idiot!»

«And you can't defend it without an army,» I said. «Would your men like to join us?»

«Sure, you earned our respect.»

«Perfect, my first order is to kill Master Conqueror.»

«They won't do it; unlike you, they have honour.»

His men proceeded to shoot him dead on the spot.

«Teabag him!» I ordered.

They did so, humiliating him. In a swear-filled rage, he retreated to his base. Throughout the next week, his enemies and we cyberbullied him until he left the game.

«Eh, a bit over the top. Kid's probably gone crying to his mum,» Bradford943 remarked.

I smirked, basking in my power. «Fucker deserved it. What do you think, Draxx?»

Draxx14 emerged from his bunker. He had been observing the battle. «Very impressive, which is why I want your skills back for the Shadow Imperium.»

«What about an alliance?» I asked.

«You're still not a true leader. I will not help you destroy shitty guilds. No glory in that.»

Our first major victory as a guild, and Draxx14 still didn't recognise us as an equal. He refused to join us in celebration. It dampened my heart.

«Forget him, mate,» Bradford943 consoled. «You came up with the plan, you led us to victory.»

«Thanks, but it was a team effort, couldn't have done it without you guys.»

«True, you'd be lost without us, lol.»

***

At the start of year nine, Charlotte contacted the headmistress of White Mountain School. The hope was for Susan to apologise so I could move on. Dad got a phone call from the headmistress.

'Have your son and his grandparents approached my school with a knife?' she asked.

'No, but an apology would help Max move on.'

'I'm not risking litigation.'

'Just a small apology then?'

'We won't take responsibility for anything in writing. But you can tell Max that Susan is very upset about how he feels.'

***

Lucas sat with me on the swing seat in the Portum garden, as I recounted what dad had told me. 'She's full of shit. Everyone knows my grandparents would never hurt anyone, let alone children.'

'I'm sorry to hear she said that.'

'Not said, she accused me of murder.'

'Well, Max, you have talked about killing Susan before.'

'Yeah, but I wouldn't kill innocent people.' We paused, using our combined strength to keep swinging forward.

'I know you're upset. But you have your entire future ahead of you. Don't spend it dwelling on Susan.'

'I spent three years with her, I can't just forget it.'

'That doesn't mean you can't move on to better things. We're super proud of you for attending all your lessons.'

'Thanks.'

'And Arthur says you're coping well without me on Friday. I'm sorry for not being in. My professor put a lot of character-modelling projects on me.'

'It's fine.'

***

Lucas and I would leave five minutes early to avoid the frantic frenzy of pupils. I drilled the times classes began into my head; that way I'd know how much time I had before the hallways became dangerous to traverse. On the one hand, I became braver, trying new foods on the high street and volunteering with Lucas, a Portum pupil and another TA to play bingo with the elderly.

Dad forced me to go on the Portum annual trip to Citadel Woods. Fortunately, I didn't have to stay the night. I'd grown up a bit since my last time there. The woods had lost their illusion of size, serving only as a small walkway. The cabin and field barely stretched half a mile. When my iPod ran out of battery and Connect Four got repetitive, I had nothing to do.

I sweltered in my coat and refused to take it off. 'I'm not eating a boring cheese sandwich. This place is dead boring.'

'Well, what would you like to do?' Lucas asked. I shrugged.

'Is there a KFC near here?' He took out his phone, opening Google Maps.

'Hold on, the signal is bad.'

'That's because we're in hell.'

'Oh, come on, it's not that awful. Why don't you go play Smash Bros. with the others?'

'Because I've never touched the game in my life.'

'You might enjoy it. Ah, here we go, there's a KFC here, but we have to drive.'

'Well, back to boredom.'

Lucas's gaze met the bus. 'I fancy KFC too. I'll ask Christine to drive us.' Christine was the assistant head in Portum. She drove us and we ate like wolves. *I don't belong here.* Three years on. Why did I still feel that way? A large part of it was my stature, thirteen years old and only four foot five.

'Woah, that is a short person,' a pupil remarked, watching me dash into Portum. My only friend was Jayden. Teaching assistants became babysitters as I dropped more and more subjects.

'How long until the lesson is over?' Not a class happened without that question.

Lucas would check his phone. 'Twenty minutes.'

I'd fidget, sweat, daydream, anything to be free of chewing-gum-filled tables and chattering pupils. I looked up ways to "grow taller" on the internet. "Live a healthier lifestyle," every site told me. I gave up after a month of not seeing immediate results. *I don't want to be six foot or whatever. Just wanna be the average.*

***

Somehow, dad and Lucas convinced me to attend an English trip. We would take part in a workshop at the Globe Theatre.

'Three pounds fifty for a map,' I gasped.

'It's expensive here, Max,' Lucas said.

'No shit, Sherlock.' The only ones from Portum in attendance, we stayed far behind the others. Heat eating away at our stamina, every step a thousand miles.

'Shakespeare is a wanker,' one pupil sniggered.

'For once I agree with them,' I said.

Lucas chuckled. 'He was clever, Max.'

'Oh, he's a genius, he wrote about love,' I dead-panned. '*Romeo and Juliet* is one of the worst things ever written. Know why?'

'Come on, I wouldn't say it's the worst.'

'I said one of the worst. It's as simple as me taking a shit, the pervert Romeo falls in love. They fuck, but oh no, their families hate each other. So after some bullshit with potions, they just die. The end.'

'I think it's deeper than that.'

'Yes, deep because he questioned family rivalry or some crap.'

'See you understand it, why not apply yourself?'

'Because in case you've forgotten, I have to give a shit for two years. Two years, one overrated story. I'd rather eat Weetabix with water.'

I couldn't see any purpose in spending two years of my life on such a "simple story".

'Seriously, Lucas, what am I supposed to learn here?'

'School is a training ground. We're trying to pre-pare you for the things you won't want to do in life.'

'So you say.'

On the way back, one of my peers gave up his seat for me on the train. 'He only did it because I'm autistic or whatever,' I whispered.

'He's being kind,' Lucas said. 'Thank you.'

I hated being reminded of my vulnerability, so much so it clouded my vision of people. My handwriting was illegible. Getting even a drop of water on my face was like being doused with gasoline and set ablaze.

I needed help to brush my teeth and hair, and electric toothbrushes were like blades. I'd only just stopped holding my dad's hair and needing pull-ups at night. Most of the time I didn't complain about appointments. They were an excuse to miss school. However, when dad arranged for occupational therapy, I wasn't over the moon.

'I'm playing Galactic Conquest, fighting side by side with my only friends.' 'Max, we're going to Naomi.'

It was ten to five, I'd only been home an hour. 'No.'

'It's helping with your body, come on, she's waiting.'

Every Tuesday, five on the dot, dragged to OT. The "clinic" wasn't far from my house. It took place in a special needs school, Naomi was the on-site occupational therapist. Rather than a school, the place resembled an overextended house. I never enjoyed being pulled away from Galactic Conquest, especially after another tiresome day of school. But eventually, I took my hood off in the sessions.

For once, when I returned home, my pale face would take on some colour, and I wouldn't lie awake for hours, unable to sleep. I suppose if you spend most of your day in a chair, your body cries out for action.

My attendance in class faded. In history, I wished we could expand on the subject, instead of the teacher playing the same video every lesson. We'd leave halfway through and return to Portum, watching history channels I liked on YouTube. It made us seem "productive", but we never followed the curriculum. I chose the time period and/or historical figure, sometimes both.

Mathematics, with every question the air became thin. Either I couldn't answer or I knew I had answered incorrectly.

***

'Lucas, get me out of here,' I pleaded.

'Shall we continue in Portum?'

I closed my burning eyes, repressing a stream of tears.

'No.' I pulled my hood-down further.

'We can do it later?'

I sprinted out of the classroom, slamming the door behind me.

'Max, wait!'

I didn't stop until I reached Portum, charging into the garden.

'Fuck this,' I screamed, hitting the punch bag. Unlike when the other boys hit it, nothing happened. *I'm weak.* Tears fell from my eyes.

'Max, I don't know what to say to you,' Lucas called. I hadn't noticed him.

'Fuck maths, it's shit. It's all shit.'

'You can't just cry when you do your GCSEs.'

'What's the fucking point? I'm not gonna do them.'

'OK, say you don't do them. What happens when something else doesn't go your way? You can't just cry, we all have to push.'

I smashed the punch bag with all my might. Nothing. 'Then I'll just have to kill myself.'

Lucas stroked his chin, picking up a pair of boxing gloves.

'How about I help you hit the punch bag? I can show you how to get it to move.'

'OK, fine.'

'Stand like this.' He adjusted my position. 'Remember, punch through the bag. You're not trying to push it.' Every punch packed more grit, a desire to rise above vulnerability. Finally, it moved. Tears exchanged for sweat.

'I did it.'

'But it was hard work, right?'

'Yeah. Wait, I see where you're going with this, I'm not going to maths again. Forget it.'

'That's your choice, I can't force you to go.'

***

Liam and, a prominent member of his clique, Aaron bounced a yoga ball around the Mondrian Room. I don't know why I'd let them in; presumably, Arthur had convinced me to give them a chance. The ball bounced off the walls; I winced at the sound. *It will hit you, leave now. No, remember what Bradford943 said: don't be paranoid.*

The yoga ball struck my head, memories overwhelmed my vision: Henry smashing me in a face with a basketball, Susan forcing me to take part in PE. All of them had taken place years ago, but it didn't matter. Calefaction engulfed my face, tears arose from somewhere blue in my throat.

'Hey, apologise!' Arthur called, interrupting the teenage boys.

'Oh, sorry, Max,' Aaron said.

'You shouldn't be throwing the ball around here, anyway. I told you to be careful, but I think you should leave.'

Both stared at each other, eyes flattened.

Arthur raised his voice slightly, 'Seriously, go.'

They shrugged, striding off. Liam whispered something in Aaron's ear, both teenagers smirked. 'Are you alright? I'm just gonna make sure they stay out, OK?'

'OK,' I sniffled.

Immediately after, I built a hidden torture chamber in Minecraft. Aaron and Liam took on the personification of villagers. Teeth gritted, I enacted my power fantasies. Above them read a sign, "Fuck Aaron and Liam, the biggest cunts in Portum." I trusted no pupil but Jayden in the Mondrian Room after that.

All subjects, including social skills with Charlotte, were abandoned. Everyone pushed for me to go back, but I didn't see any reason to. I spent the lessons staring at the clock. The journey to and from pained me, I didn't see an academic future for myself. I preferred confiding in Galactic Conquest, writing stories, and learning "cool tricks" with computers.

The way I saw it, I had talents that school wouldn't benefit. To survive and "have a purpose", I needed to go my own way. No more *Romeo and Juliet*, no more fearing for my safety. I'd do exactly what I wanted, when I wanted, safe from vulnerability in my own little bubble.

Chapter 12: Grievances

'Max, please put the knife down,' Charlotte called.

I pointed my weapon at her.

'Where the fuck is Susan? When the fuck is she coming in?' I exploded. 'I'm going to fucking murder her. I-I'll kill her and send her family the body.'

'Come on, little man. Let's just go back to Minecraft,' Arthur appealed.

I clutched the knife. Images of Susan shouting at me thundered in front of my eyes.

'I'm gonna do what I should have done years ago. Stab her in the fucking heart.'

'We can't have you hurting anyone in Portum,' Charlotte stressed. 'Please, please, stop.'

'Not even that cunt? Someone needs to gouge her fucking eyes out,' I cried. Out of an animalistic desire for loosely defined justice, I'd burn up, then my body became numb. *In your dreams, Grotty.* The words echoed, penetrating my soul. Through eyes misty with tears, I peered at my weapon. I'd torture Susan, cutting open her eyelids. She would beg for death.

'He's stopped,' a TA whispered. *Still can't do it. Too weak.* The knife crashed out of my hand, smashing onto the floor. I charged to the Mondrian Room, engulfed in my hoodie. Susan laughed, her piercing blue eyes still in their sockets. *Should have stabbed her years ago.*

The door creaked open; I raised my fists. One last stand against tyranny, I'd do all I could to hurt her. Shaking, I glanced up to find Charlotte striding past. She lay on the beanbag.

'Oh, this is very comfortable. You know, you're very lucky to have this room.' Slowly, my fists loosened. 'What do you want?'

'I can come back later. Would you like me to do that?'

'Just tell me what you want.'

'I want you to know that Susan isn't coming in. It's just prospective parents from the school.'

'Oh.'

'Do you have a problem with them?'

'No.'

'Oh good. But you know, Max, carrying a knife is a criminal offence. Someone might get seriously hurt, including you.'

'Yeah.'

'We want everyone to be safe in Portum. And I want you to know that you're safe, you don't need a weapon.'

'OK, sure.'

'It also makes others feel unsafe. We don't want that.'

Pushed down the stairs and almost trampled, my sanctuary invaded, no perceived way to stand up for myself. *It's alright for her, she's a teacher.*

'I won't do it again. I get it, carrying knives is bad.'

'Good. And you'll never need to.'

'Why, because I'm safe in Portum?'

'No, because Susan isn't allowed in Portum, at least not while you're here.'

'Really?'

'Yes really. While you're here, she's not allowed in Portum.'

'What about when she is here?'

'Everyone will make it clear you don't want to speak to her.'

Part of me still desired confrontation, justice. None of my anger had subsided. All I saw was lip service from Charlotte. I didn't feel safe in Portum and believed only "justice" could stop my anger.

***

'I think it's a good idea if you move to the kitchen,' Lucas suggested. 'Then we can work towards removing your coat?'

'Remember what happened last time you removed my hood?' I hinted.

'You weren't ready. And I made a mistake.' He paused, laughing nervously. 'But you can't wear a coat forever, Max. That's not how it works out there, and we have to prepare you.'

I looked around the Mondrian Room; I saw the memories we had made here. 'It's not gonna be that easy, Lucas.'

'Nothing in life is easy. Like I said, school is a training ground. We're here to help you survive out there.'

If I left, would I be safe? Rowdiness always echoed from the kitchen. *Nothing stopping me from coming back here.*

'On three conditions. First, I'm not taking off my coat. Second, if it sucks, I'll come back here. Third, I'm bringing my laptop.'

'Yes, fair enough. I'm so proud of you, Max.' I chose a spot on the sofa furthest out of the way. One near a socket to charge my laptop. The kitchen served as my base, but nothing changed, I didn't attend any lessons, ignored everyone else and did my own thing.

***

One morning, I found my laptop missing. My heart climbed into my throat.

'Have any of you seen my laptop?' I asked.

'No, have you tried the Mondrian Room?' a TA replied.

'Thanks.' *Doesn't make sense, I always leave it here.*

It wasn't in the Mondrian Room.

'Someone may have stolen it,' an older boy chuckled.

'Carlos, if you have it, I will kill you.' He waltzed off, laughing. *Because it isn't enough they bully people over*

Smash Bros. Jayden told me Carlos was a "bullshitter," but I couldn't shake the fear of him having it. When something was stolen or went missing in Portum, the owner seldom recovered it.

Lucas found me turning the Mondrian Room upside down, desperately searching for the device I so craved. 'Max, I heard you're upset about your laptop.'

'Has Carlos the cunt stolen it?'

'No, why are you angry with Carlos?'

'Because he's a twat.'

Lucas sighed. 'We took it to the IT guy. You've been accessing inappropriate websites. It's stopping you from going to class.'

'You've seen me use the internet. I only use a proxy server to browse Reddit. Does Charlotte think I'm watching porn or some shit?'

'Charlotte wanted to ban you from using it completely. But Arthur and I persuaded her not to.'

'This is bullshit.'

'I'm sorry, I didn't think it would upset you so much. You'll have it back this afternoon.'

I waited for hours in boredom until the IT guy finally arrived. 'Did you remove it?' Lucas asked.

'Yeah,' the IT guy replied.

'You realise I'll just install it again, right?' I chided.

'Good luck trying,' the IT guy said.

'Max, if you install it again, we'll have to take the laptop permanently,' Lucas warned.

'Why? That's such crap.'

'I like it when you do productive things like writing stories. But a lot of us in Portum feel it's disruptive. I know you enjoy Disturbed, but you can't play music in school. We're here to learn, it's your training ground.'

'I'm impressed, Max. I found a calculator you made, can you program?' the IT guy asked.

'No, I just followed a tutorial on the internet.'

'Really? Well, you'd be good at IT, it's a big field. You might end up in technical support like me.'

'No, I'm shit at IT, besides all we ever did in class was Excel.'

'If you'd applied yourself, I think you'd have found it interesting,' Lucas said.

I spent the rest of the day undoing the IT guy's handiwork. This time I didn't share my password with Lucas. The Portum staff no longer held leverage over my laptop.

They and my parents feared I'd sink into a greater downward spiral. The laptop prevented that; taking it away would invoke resentment, and not a new found desire to attend my lessons .

These were not the only issues I had to deal with. Rising concerns about my weight, including the question of whether I'd even go through puberty at all, meant I got referred to a feeding clinic. Dad and I would go there on a Tuesday, once a month.

I made sure I was downstairs at least ten minutes before he arrived. I didn't want to be seen in school with my parents. (This is also why I never attended after-school events at Portum.) We'd go to Carluccio's and I'd eat as much as I could. Then we went to the clinic, they weighed me, took my height, and asked to observe me eating with dad.

I had to eat different foods, but at some point, I brought up Susan and how much I "hated her". So besides diagnosing me with an eating-disorder, they scolded dad for allowing me to "talk like that".

'You have to be careful what you say out there,' dad warned. *She hurt me. Why can't I talk about it?*

It was yet another reason to retreat online, though even there things were difficult. School killed the free time of just about everyone in my guild. The computer of one of my best generals broke down. Meanwhile, Draxx14 had left for university, leaving the Shadow Imperium to decay. In a last-ditch effort to save it, he merged with the remnants of the Devil Dogs.

This will require an exposition dump, so bear with me. A year prior to this, the leader of The Devil Dogs, arguably the most successful guild on Galactic Conquest, left to join the military. He gave Diablous034 and Invicta11 leadership of the guild's remnants.

133

For a year they struggled, as inevitably larger guilds would rise to take their place. Glory days over, they'd soon be a footnote in the memories of a few teenagers. Guess who risked the same fate? Draxx14, one of their best warriors. Out of past loyalties, the remnants of the Devil Dogs merged with the larger body under the Shadow Imperium banner.

Diablous034 and Invicta11 didn't follow. Nobody knows why. Instead of them, Major279 took command of the Shadow Imperium. He was one of Draxx14's mentors and closest friends. Though he didn't take up official leadership, he might as well have done. Draxx14 didn't have time to fulfil the role whilst at university.

Major279 shared power with Lemons43, one of the old guard. And despite Draxx14's professed distaste for "instant promotions", he granted Devil Dog veterans positions they hadn't earned. Established members of the Shadow Imperium were demoted and replaced. And if they so much as protested, Major279 executed them under firing squad. He was determined to suppress what the Shadow Imperium used to be. Starboy23, our former leader, was stripped of all power and relevance. Former generals took orders from Devil Dog veterans.

The Devil Dogs believed in "purity". Anyone who didn't meet their standards got abused and kicked out of the guild. In short, they took over the Shadow Imperium with Draxx14's consent, and out of a longing for their glory days, they re-created it in their own image. The grievances of Shadow Imperium members didn't matter, The Devil Dogs were here to stay. People came to me for help.

«You're the only one who listens,» they said.

I hated Major279 and his notion of a "perfect soldier"; when I was in the Devil Dogs, he'd shoot me for no reason. I didn't have a big enough army, and most of my men were stuck in school. I had to play the long game. That involved finding new allies, accumulating funds, and getting a more respectable base. Not only that, I'd need people to view me as the legitimate leader of Shadow Imperium veterans.

Throughout Christmas, I bided my time, building a bigger powerbase. Patience gave me an advantage. The situation in the Shadow Imperium got worse, which meant intervention became more justified.

Sometimes I'd purposefully instigate things, bait Major279 and his men into traps. Though I knew better, they'd attack me for what appeared to others as "no reason"; it made them look like the aggressors. This caused people to view them in a negative light, thus stoking further resentment. My goal was to turn that resentment into an army, and my efforts were bearing fruit. When Major279 abused someone, we had another soldier. I recruited new generals like IMaginkI, a computer science student at university, and proficient in more programming languages than

I can count on my fingers; and even Starboy23, who abandoned the Shadow Imperium, further legitimising my cause.

Bradford943 still served as my second-in-command. Soon it would be time to light the spark. I journeyed to the Shadow Imperium base on a "diplomatic mission". My true intentions were to recruit people and gain sympathisers. Major279 must have noticed people leaving for the Paladins. He killed me when I walked past; I didn't defend myself; I wanted to paint him as the aggressor. Therefore, his assassination would be justified. "I Will Not Bow" by Breaking Benjamin blasted from my speakers. *Here we go.* One of Major279's guards was my mole; he pretended not to notice me.

«Right face,» Major279 ordered. His men obeyed, executing each formation with unrivalled precision. I hurled a grenade at Major279's face. The explosion threw his mangled corpse into the air.

«A little present from me,» I called, darting off.

«Kill him on sight,» Major279 boomed. «Whoever brings me his head gets a promotion.»

I fell back into a narrow tunnel, an ideal place to use my mini-gun. Bradford943 sent me a message over Skype.

«Did you kill him?»

«Yeah, here's a screenshot.»

«Careful, we don't want to provoke them too much.»

«I'm just here to get propaganda for recruitment.» Footsteps fluttered in the distance. «And I'm gonna get a lot more.»

Four commandos charged my position. The quiet tunnel erupted in a furious firefight. I didn't stop shooting, not until their muzzle flashes fell silent. My weapon smoked, unable to fire another shot. Close to death, I gazed at the fallen commandos. *Holy shit, I killed them.* They accused me of cheating. The entire chat spewed toxicity. I'd proven the Devil Dogs weren't invincible, we could defeat even their best. But my actions weren't without consequences. Hours later, Draxx14 contacted me on Skype.

«XMA, what the actual fuck,» Draxx14 fumed. My heart sank, I didn't want to make enemies with a friend. I believed he was being manipulated by Major279, and that he would eventually come around to my way of thinking.

«What do you mean?» I asked.

«Don't bullshit me.» He sent a screenshot; it was a message from Major279.

«XMA killed us all without provocation.»

«If I hear of you pulling this shit again, I will blow the Paladins to HELL. Do you understand? HELL.»

«It was self-defence, look.» I showed him my evidence.

«You just proved you did it.»

«What was I supposed to do, let them kill me?»

«You're supposed to stay out of our way. Last chance, don't bother me again.» The Paladins couldn't take on the Devil Dogs, they'd overrun our lines with sheer numbers. When I defeated their commandos, the terrain was to my advantage. We didn't have the resources to wage war, nor did I want to fight Draxx14. We'd created something together. How could I destroy it?

Occupational therapy with Naomi made a difference. I could catch myself if I tripped over. I didn't wear my coat in our sessions. OT helped me with my reflexes, giving me a chance against the Devil Dog commandos. Naomi introduced it to my timetable and instructed Lucas. Portum didn't have many facilities, so we used the kitchen in the mornings. Without equipment, we had to invent our own exercises. Each one had a different purpose. Some strengthened my oral muscles, others built upper-body strength. I'd fall silent and slow down if another Portum student entered the room.

The exercises helped me, so why would I be embarrassed? Weakness or fear of weakness; I didn't want to show I needed help. I got enough reminders of that on the stairs, barely able to keep up with the flood.

***

One afternoon, when Arthur and I were going down to the bus at home time, we got caught in the tidal wave.

Arthur rushed downstairs, believing I was following behind, but other students pushed in front. Unable to pass, I got caught in the rat run, knocked from side to side, forced to endure a tsunami of screaming. We filtered out like an annoyingly slow drip from a sieve; I wasn't strong enough to break through, and I didn't trust in the kindness of those before me. *I'm a sitting duck out here.* A rush of air, testosterone-filled laughter. Someone lifted my hood. I turned to find two year elevens towering above me, the tallest I'd seen. They had sickening smiles.

'What you gonna do, kid?'

Legs trembling, I raised my fists. They both laughed cruelly, mocking my weakness. *No, you'll lose.* I pulled my hood back on and rushed downstairs, pushing with all my might.

'Shall we do it again? Lift his hood?'

'Wait till he goes down.'

Big mistake, Arthur overheard them. 'Did they lift your hood?' he asked.

I nodded, choking back the tears.

His eyebrows furrowed. 'Alright, go to the bus. I'll deal with them.' I ran but stopped when I overheard Arthur confronting them. Their laughter faded. Faced with a teacher, they had nowhere to run.

'I-I'll be nice,' one of them pleaded. 'See, I'll hold the door open.'

Arthur motioned for me to keep running. I did so, not stopping until I reached the bus.

139

'Max, did something happen?' Jayden asked.

'Cunts,' I sniffled.

'Probably mainstreamers,' one of the older boys guessed. 'He's not the first.'

Arthur jumped onto the bus, rushing over to me. 'Are you alright? I've dealt with it, they're in big trouble.'

Blood pounded in my ears; my body jittered with chilling melancholy. 'Who are they? I want to fucking kill them, and their families,' I shouted. 'I will destroy everything they love. I'll torture their parents right in front of their eyes.'

Arthur gently placed his hand on my back. 'Hey, it's alright. I left them with their form tutor.'

'Those bastards,' Jayden remarked. 'Are they gonna kick them out?'

'I can't tell you that,' Arthur replied.

'Doesn't matter, if I see them again I'm getting a knife,' I cried. 'I want them dead.'

Later, at home, I logged on Galactic Conquest. Having people who understood and respected me stopped the tears.

'They're just cunts who can't get any pussy,' Bradford943 said. 'If I was there, they'd be dead.'

It was a nice thought, the Paladins assailing my tormentors. Were my power to extend into the real world, we'd guard Portum as we did our base and enforce "decency" on the stairs.

'Charlotte told me what happened,' dad said. 'I'm very sorry.'

I didn't see him coming in. 'It's fine.'

'It's not your fault, they're high-jinks boys looking for a laugh. It could have been anyone. You know how kids are.'

'It's bullshit.'

'Unfortunately, that's how the world is. Shall I get mum to make you a hot chocolate?'

'Yes.'

The next morning, I sat down with Lucas and Charlotte.

'I can arrange for them to come up and apologise. Would you like that?' Charlotte offered.

'Don't worry, we won't leave you alone with them,' Lucas added.

'If you can't trust them alone with me, they shouldn't be anywhere near Portum.'

'Alright, fine, they won't come up,' Charlotte said. 'You know, Max, it's really important we all feel safe here.'

'You always say that.'

'I know, but it's still very important,' she chuckled. 'I'm going to have an assembly with the year elevens today, it's about autism. And I think it will make everyone in school safer and more understanding.'

'If they had a choice, they wouldn't go. The moment you leave the cunts.'

'Language,' she interjected.

I sighed. 'They're just gonna say horrible things behind our backs.'

'Maybe, Max, maybe. But if one of them walks away kinder, it's an accomplishment.'

The "high-jinks boys" ended up being expelled for setting off the fire alarm one time too many, bringing much needed relief to the Portum students who despised the noise.

Chapter 13: Two Worlds

31.3.16

«I'd like to thank everyone in The Paladins. Without you I wouldn't be here. When I first started, I knew nothing. Now I've learnt so much about myself and all of you, every brother and sister. I hope that one day, in the future, you'll look upon your time spent here fondly. To celebrate this occasion, every one of you here who is eligible will be promoted. Congratulations to us all for achieving 100 members, and here's to 100 more.»

The pride of the Paladins brought a smile to my face. We had members in the United Kingdom, the United States, France, Belgium, and even far-away India. By this point, we'd fought highly skilled players and won, fended off attacks from Major279, and survived the school term, something which normally kills off a guild's activity as it renders most of their members without sufficient time to play the game.

Easter holidays meant people would be on their computers more. A time for us to move towards my goal of becoming one of the most powerful players on Galactic Conquest. With help from my friends, I knew I'd achieve it. 'You waste your brain,' everyone told me; without GC-SEs, how could the world measure my "intelligence"?

Well, I'm using my brain here. I'd like to see dad try leading the Paladins.

***

One night, Major279 attacked us and almost overwhelmed our defences. Because his men were in another time zone, they took advantage of Bradford943 and I being asleep at 3 am. Fortunately, we had troops from many countries.

«You're a stubborn scrub,» Bradford943 chided. «It's worth negotiating an alliance with the Shadow Imperium. At least for now.»

«We won't be able to poach their members anymore,» I replied.

«That's the point, you're pissing them off too much. Besides, we can't risk them winning next time.»

«I'll give your idea a chance. But I don't trust Major.»

«Neither do I, but you get all paranoid around them. You'll stop worrying, they'll stop worrying, and if we go to war they'll help us. Nothing bad here.»

Despite getting a headache from it all, I attended the negotiations. Lemons43 agreed to a formal alliance and all our terms. Major279 stormed off, called me "cancerous" and left. I never saw him again, and Lemons43 took over his duties. Out of loyalty to Draxx14, the Devil Dogs stayed in the Shadow Imperium. Both sides stuck to the agreed treaty. For a while, there were never any problems. And we'd need that alliance, because a few days later I received this message:

7.4.16

«Your officer Senseipig has spoken outwardly rude to me by saying, 'Our group is better that yours. We will crush you like the bugs you are.'

War is coming, be ready.

King Dominator»

Senseipig was staying with his family in a rural area with no internet connection. He wasn't due to return until the fourteenth of that month. Because we were a small guild, King Dominator believed he'd overwhelm us with sheer numbers. It wouldn't matter if I protested; all we could do was prepare.

***

«XMA, that's Warped_Paradox»' Bradford943 pointed out.

«The one with 2000 members in his guild?» I asked, starstruck.

«Yep.»

«Why's he at our base?»

'We'll find out.'

«XMA, greetings,» Warped_Paradox said. «I hope your reputation proceeds you. I'm going to propose an alliance.»

«Why?» I queried. «We're smaller than you.»

«You beat AFS and held back the Shadow Imperium. Now one of my potential rivals is attacking you. Why wouldn't I want to help?»

«I didn't beat AFS on my own. My general Vish09 led the defence.»

«All the same to me, great leaders produce great generals. My spies report King Dominator is raiding you tonight, so I'm sending troops to support you.»

«Can't turn that down,» Bradford943 remarked.

«Indeed.» I showed Warped_Paradox and his arriving entourage to the meeting room.

«Without us you'd have lost. Congratulations for making the right decision.»

«Thanks,» I replied. «How does King Dominator fight?»

«Good question. Most of his men are new players, they joined because they're stupid. He just sends them to die without thought.»

«That makes our job easier. We'll have a defensive line to distract them, while snipers on the cliffs thin their numbers.»

«Is this why we always have cliffs?» Bradford943 asked. «Someone's gonna catch on.»

«They haven't yet, lol,» I replied.

«It's better we have three defensive lines,» Warped_Paradox said.

«They're gonna charge us, one should be enough.»

«First, all battles last twenty minutes. Whoever controls the capture point at the end wins.»

«Delay tactics then?»

«Now you're catching on. Second, if they die at the landing zone, they'll respawn and regroup too easily. If they're deeper into the valley, it will take longer to get reinforcements.»

We waited in the ghostly mists atop pitch-black terrain. All of us wore dark armour as camouflage.

«They're coming,» one of our men called. They charged us, a classical human-wave tactic. Laser blasts and vilifications were flung by both sides. The explosion of several grenades deafened my music.

«Who's using the pussy-ass mini-gun?» King Dominator shouted.

«Me, you daft cunt,» I jabbed.

He respawned, instantly falling victim to sniper fire.

«Fight me like a man XMA.»

«I would, but you're a child.»

Though our enemies lacked skill, they made up for it in numbers. They pushed us back, defensive line after defensive line.

«Lol, u guys fucking suck,» King Dominator taunted. The capture point glowed in front of him. «Bye-bye Paladins.»

Just as he sent that message, time ran out. "TWEN-TY MINUTES EXCEEDED; THE PALADINS HAVE DEFEND-ED SUCCESSFULLY."

Before they could utter a word, the game expelled our enemy. They wouldn't be able to attack again until tomorrow.

«We only won because he wasted time boasting,» I said.

«A victory is a victory, just accept it. We need to counter-attack before he does,» Warped_Paradox replied.

«It's 11pm, XMA and I are in the UK,» Brad-ford943 explained. «So that will be tomorrow.»

«Fine, do you have Discord?»

«Discord? We have Skype.»

«It's a new messaging site. Make an account and join my guild's server. We'll discuss plans there.»

At the time of writing, Discord is widespread. Back in 2016, most guilds still used Skype for communication. Warped_Paradox had been a guild leader for years, he was nineteen and a graphics-design student, which to a bunch of teenagers was godlike. He made excellent propaganda and taught me a few tricks too. The Shadow Imperium un-der Lemons43 honoured our alliance. Together, our three guilds had the numbers for a frontal assault.

***

«IMaginkI has King Dominator's IP Address,» I announced. «He lives in the same city as Starboy23.»

148

«I don't want someone hurting him in real life or doxing him,» Warped_Paradox said.

«Can we at least shut off his internet?»

«If you want.»

«IMaginkI, do it, mate.»

«I can do only it for five minutes.»

«Do it just before we attack. Let us cause them a bit of chaos,» Warped_Paradox said.

IMaginkI overwhelmed King Dominator's router with information, tearing down his internet connection. That meant he wouldn't be able to rally his men when we attacked.

'Turn it down,' mum called. 'I'm on the phone.'

'I told you, I need to hear who's shooting at me,' I replied. Enemies swarmed our position, I provided covering fire with my mini-gun.

She groaned. 'If you only focused that well in school.'

«Sir, two on your left.» a Paladin exclaimed.

I turned, gunning them down. «Good eye. Let's grab the capture point,» I said.

«Already got it XMA,» Warped_Paradox called. «Just need to hold.»

Fifteen minutes late, King Dominator arrived. «Sorry guys, my parents have shit internet.»

The on-screen countdown began. Five minutes until our coalition won, and King Dominator knew it. «You fucking bastards. Kill yourselves!» He screamed.

«Your mum sucks cock for a living,» Warped_Paradox retorted.

«Fuck you. Leave now, my dad's a cop and he can have you all arrested.»

«Yeah, and my dad works for the FBI,» I sassed.

As we closed in, enemy morale crumbled. King Dominator begged and pleaded with us to stop killing him. It brought a smile to my face. We recorded the whole thing.

«Wait, I have to go for lunch,» King Dominator cried, logging off.

«Starboy, is it lunch-time in Texas?» I asked.

«Nope.»

«He's a coward,» Warped_Paradox remarked.

I addressed King Dominator's men. «Your leader left you all to die. Join the Paladins, we won't treat you like garbage.»

«Why recruit them? They are garbage,» Warped_Paradox challenged. «Unless you want more cannon-fodder.»

«We'll teach them to be better at the game,» I replied. With his base ransacked, and his men defecting to the Paladins, King Dominator's empire fell to anarchy. I took great pride in tormenting him until it got boring. The Shadow Imperium entered a permanent alliance with us. Rather than aimlessly fighting each other, we realised the benefits of cooperation.

Three hundred members under my belt, new alliances and a greater reputation. Then school started again, and I was subject to the stairs. Lucas tried to engage me with cooking in Portum. I learnt valuable skills from it, but someone else did most of the work for me. Besides that and playing bingo with the elderly, I didn't do anything productive in school. I still didn't see the purpose in academia. Why spend years of my life on *Romeo and Juliet*? How did it prove my intelligence? Galactic Conquest may have been virtual, but at least I felt like I was achieving things there and learning things I couldn't in school. My parents didn't understand it, and I told no one at Portum.

***

'I'm not going to Maths it sucks,' I declared.

Lucas took a deep breath. 'I can't force you to go.' He paused. 'Did something happen in your guild? You're not talking to me.'

My body jerked upward. 'How the hell do you know about my guild?'

'Your dad told me, he said you have 300 members. I'm really impressed.'

'Damn it, he's not supposed to say anything.'

'Why, what's the problem?'

'I don't want anyone in Portum knowing. I'd like to keep my online stuff separate. Besides if my enemies find out I'm autistic—'

'Your enemies? You have enemies?'

'Never mind.'

'If you have a problem, I can help. I used to—'

'Here, I'll just show you.' I navigated to YouTube, showing him our guild's recruitment video.

When he saw us in battle, his jaw dropped. 'This is awesome, we have a lot of students who would love—'

'You can't tell anyone. Nobody at Portum can join me, not even Jayden.'

'I won't, but I still don't understand why.'

'It's too dangerous for them. And I want to keep it separate.'

Paranoia and a desire to guard a haven outside of school drove my decision. Only Bradford943 knew of Portum. I trusted him but feared other players outside the Paladins would attack me for having a "diagnosis". If Portum students joined, they might expose my actual identity (accidentally or on purpose). However well-intentioned their inclusion, I didn't want to risk anyone being doxed.

***

'I only told them because I'm proud,' dad said. 'They should know about your achievement.'

'You told Charlotte too? Now she's gonna try getting me to make friends over it or some crap,' I fretted.

'She won't, I'll tell her not to.'

***

'Your dad told you about this, right?' Lucas asked. He held a letter from Susan, addressed to me.

'Yeah.'

'Before you open it...' he paused. 'Remember that it might not be the closure you want.'

'I know. Let's just get it over with.'

He gave me the letter. I slowly tore the envelope open. My pupils dilated. *She doesn't care. She hurt me and she doesn't even care.*

'What does it say?' Lucas asked.

'She won't apologise.'

'If it's upsetting you, I suggest you bin it.'

I nodded, ripping the letter in two. 'Wish we could set it on fire.'

Into the bin it went. Never to be seen again. I couldn't see myself getting over what happened in primary school. The memories of Susan were too strong, and the letter certainly didn't help things. Three years had passed, but I still suffered nightmares.

Lots of fears lurked in my subconscious. Losing my guild was one of them. In the dreams, either my account got hacked or I lost the respect of my friends. I'd wake up in a pool of sweat, praying life wouldn't destroy my achievement. One night, I misunderstood one of Bradford943's messages.

«I'm gonna take over, lol,» he said. The message wasn't serious, but on the internet you can't always tell.

153

Paranoid, I told my other generals to "prepare a surprise" in case he tried anything. The message got leaked, and Bradford943 blocked me on every form of contact.

The Paladins neared 400 members; our patrols often exceeded twenty people at a time. I didn't want people to lose respect or see me as incompetent. So I lied about what had happened.

23.6.16

«[Alert] Someone has given us false intel. They told us Bradford wants to take over The Light Paladins. Please ignore any rumours or theories, we're sure Bradford will return soon.»

Self-deception didn't settle. Guilt grabbed my heart. Warped_Paradox started an investigation, they questioned everyone. Judas64, one of my generals, carried out his own investigation. After a day or two, I told both him and Warped_Paradox the truth, but they never responded to my messages on Discord or Skype.

27.6.16

«All online troops come to patrol, I have a surprise for XMA.» – Judas64.

I'd admitted the truth last night. Why hadn't he announced it? A "surprise?" It seemed like a trap to me. I went to base anyway, there was no point hiding. Judas64 and Warped_Paradox approached me upon arrival. They had my own men arrest me.

«I didn't do anything,» I pleaded. «Is this about my message?»

«You're on trial, we'll give you five minutes to prepare,» Warped_Paradox said. *It's my guild. Why can you put me on trial?* I wanted to disappear, travel back in time and fix my mistake. A tear landed on my desk, next to my mug.

The judges were Judas64 and Warped_Paradox. Surrounding me were my men. Bradford943 watched from a far corner.

«Time's up, explain yourself or we sentence you to death,» Warped_Paradox threatened. «Judas will lead the Paladins. And you will give him leadership immediately.»

«The trial hasn't started,» I said. «What am I charged with?»

«Betrayal,» Judas64 replied.

«How am I a traitor?»

«You framed Bradford.»

«It was a misunderstanding, I sent you both messages last night.»

«I didn't get anything.»

«I have screenshots of me sending the messages. Why would I lie?»

«Because you're corrupt.»

I thought my heart would explode. Both fear and betrayal are soul-destroying. I turned around, addressing my men in the jury. «Have I ever let you down?»

«They aren't allowed to speak,» Warped_Paradox interjected.

«Why not? It's their guild as much as it's mine, and as their leader I'm open to their judgement.» I didn't know what I was harnessing, or where I was going. «When I was younger, people locked me in tiny rooms. The Paladins is my way of escaping those memories. I'd never do anything to ruin what we've built.»

«Bullshit,» Judas64 accused.

«I made a mistake, I took one of Bradford's messages out of context. I was too ashamed to admit it. I've got proof, please forgive me.»

«Is that it?» Warped_Paradox queried.

«Yes, but whatever decision you make, I'm not giving the Paladins to Judas.»

«If you don't, we'll kill you until you do.»

«All I need to do is switch off my computer, there's nothing you can do about it,» I retorted. My eyes were blinded with tears; I plead with the universe for mercy.

«We will take time to decide your fate,» Warped_Paradox said.

«I thought it was up to my friends.»

«They aren't your friends anymore. And we'll decide whether they like it or not.»

Two blood-freezing minutes passed. Then, «Our decision is as follows. XMA24 must transfer leadership to Judas64.»

A bitter outcome, but amidst the melancholy I received a message on Skype from Judas64's brother. He'd sent screenshots, proof that Judas64 was using the situation to stage a coup. Through a simple action, he had saved my guild, my reason for being. Bradford943 forgave me, Warped_Paradox left, blocked me, and never spoke to me again. And though destabilised, our guild would soon return to normalcy.

As for Judas64, I got his password from his brother. Only after he grovelled and paid a hefty ransom did I return the account. Years later, whilst doing research for this book, I learnt that Warped_Paradox had conspired with Judas64. He had wanted to turn the Paladins into a vassal army, led by someone loyal to him. Honestly, in hindsight this doesn't surprise me. Galactic Conquest could be unforgiving, people were always trying to outmanoeuvre each other.

For me, exposure to hierarchy and betrayal didn't come through the real world. I learnt my hardest lessons online.

Chapter 14: Bubbling

'Give me five more minutes,' I called.

'No, it's bloody late. Forget it,' dad shouted.

'Fine, two more minutes then.' I turned back to Galactic Conquest, typing a message. «Did you phone them? The suicide prevention line?»

«Yes, thank you, XMA,» my general replied.

Dad pulled the door open, marching over to the computer. 'Turn it off now.'

'No, fuck off!' I cried.

'You've got to stop that stupid game.' He pushed me out of the way, switching off the machine.

'What the fuck, dad.' I jumped up, punching him in the face.

'Can't you see it's destroying you!? Punch me all you like, you can't always get your own way.'

'I just saved someone from—'

'I don't care if you saved the Queen of England. Get to bed.'

With a clenched jaw, I lunged at him. A blur of smoky tears and pounding headaches. The next day at school, I tried to forget about it. Hopefully, my friend and loyal general was OK. I hadn't spoken to him since dad had pulled me away the night before.

Lucas and I were playing a game on my laptop. We didn't notice Charlotte coming in.

'What are you up to?' she asked, smiling. In her hands, she carried a whiteboard and marker.

'We're playing flash games,' I replied, focused on the screen.

'Flash games?'

'They're computer games,' Lucas said.

'Right, OK. Can you pause?'

Let's get this over with. 'Fine, we'll pause. What do you want?'

She sat down, writing something on the whiteboard. *Is this another lecture about kindness?* 'Now then, your dad told me you were very upset at a game last night.' *Upset? Only because dad got in the way.*

'No, I was helping someone. Why would I get upset?'

'Well...'

'Don't you preach about helping people? Or are you a hypocrite?'

'Do you know what that means?'

'Yes, why else would I use the word?'

'Oh, is the game about helping people? That's positive and kind.'

'I've been playing for two years, it's more important than school.'

'You know, it's actually very important you come to school.'

'It's your education, Max,' Lucas added.

'Yes, It is your education, and we want to help you. Have you heard of Maslow's hierarchy of needs?' Charlotte asked.

'No.'

She drew a layered pyramid. 'It's a way of knowing what responsibilities to prioritise in life.' She pointed to the first layer. 'What do you think goes here?'

'Stuff that keeps me alive.' She filled in the first layer. 'Get to the point. You think school is more important than what I do.'

'You're clever, and you know education is more important than—'

'It isn't. You don't know what I do, you wouldn't even understand it.'

'I understand it,' Lucas interjected. 'I used to play these games.'

'Yeah, but you did nothing like this,' I replied.

'I don't have to understand it,' Charlotte rebutted. 'All we want is you safe and happy at Portum. Computer games aren't part of that.'

Bullshit. Fortunately, my friend was OK, we kept playing like nothing ever happened.

***

'We need to talk about Galactic Conquerors,' dad said.

'It's Galactic Conquest,' I corrected.

'Right, Galactic Conquest. When you have a problem, talk to me.'

You wouldn't listen last night. 'I've been doing this for years, I can handle it. Besides, it's not only me running the Paladins, I have help.'

'Then what's stopping you making another friend at school?'

There he goes, changing the subject.

'I have Jayden. And all my friends in The Paladins.'

He looked at my screen, trying to perceive what was going on. 'What makes you enjoy that game so much? It's just people walking around.'

'I have nothing else.'

'What about Portum? It's lovely when you're with Jayden and Lucas.'

The stairs at school terrified me, and I never thought I'd amount to anything academically. I found such fears too embarrassing to admit, and I didn't want my parents to worry. The Paladins was my greatest achievement, it gave me a reason to live. But how could an outsider understand its value?

Dad sighed. 'Never mind.' He stood up, walking to the door. 'We're trying to transfer your statement to an EHCP. So it'd be good if you aimed for at least two GCSEs.' I had no idea what an EHCP was (it's an Education, Health and Care Plan), nor did I see myself doing any GCSEs. Besides, more "pressing" things were transpiring online.

Apologies in advance, but it's time for another exposition dump. Back in early June of that year, Draxx14 had briefly returned. He found the Shadow Imperium in tatters. Major279 had left, and Lemons43 wasn't "good enough" for the Devil Dog veterans. On request from Draxx14, Diablous034 and Invicta11 took his place. As most of the guild's original members joined me, the Shadow Imperium became a vessel for the Devil Dog veterans to continue their legacy.

Diablous034's first act was tearing up the alliance between our guilds. He and his men didn't believe we were "pure soldiers." And despite Lemons43's efforts to normalise relations, he and the Devil Dog veterans didn't want to associate with us. Against my better instincts, I went to their base to "smooth things over".

***

«No, why would we ally with cancer?» Diablous034 mocked.

«We're actual soldiers, we don't have time for kids who think they can do something.» Invicta11 jabbed.

«If you're so pure, why did your leader abandon you?» I retorted.

«That's where you're wrong, XMA,» Diablous034 rebutted. «We've always embodied real soldiers. The Devil Dogs have a legacy to uphold, and we won't tarnish it by allying with you.»

«Are you declaring war on us instead?»

«No, we're not aggressive like you.»

«Tell you what,» Invicta11 said. «Expel that dyslexic retard from your commandos, and we might take you seriously.»

«Take that back!» I demanded. «Now!»

«We're just calling you out for what you are: cancerous rejects.»

I stepped closer and one of Invicta11's guards fired a warning shot. Chaos ensued, a violent firefight rocking the screen. We held our own until they outflanked us.

The Paladins received a lot of cryptic threats that summer, but we couldn't prove it was the Shadow Imperium. Blocking them in game didn't stop them attacking our base, so by resisting their provocations we hoped they'd get bored and leave us alone.

***

I'd just started year ten and I was running out of time.

'You need to do Maths and English, that's three GCSES. But we need you to pick two more subjects,' dad explained.

'I'll do RE and Media, I guess,' I replied.

'Remember, climb the ladder. If you don't pass five, you can't stay at Portum. And because there aren't any other placements, you'll have to stay at home.'

'Oh. More time for Galactic Conquest then,'

'Forget that, you're going to a school no matter what. You've got a chance other children would kill for. Don't blow it.'

'Come on, please don't send me to residential. I'd rather stay at Portum.'

'Don't climb the ladder, and you might end up in a school you hate.'

I looked at the doorway, longing for my computer. *Hopefully Bradford943 handled those raiders OK.*

'Listen, Max. It's happened to other children, and we don't want it to happen to you. Work with Lucas, he knows what's coming down the line.'

'Why can't I just stay at home?'

'Because you're a bright boy. We're trying to help you, why can't you see it?'

Five subjects, most students took more. It sounded reasonable on paper. Pass them all and get into sixth form. With fear of a residential placement as my motivator, I tried to attend class. Everyone encouraged me to better myself, even Bradford943. I attended all my subjects, and on some days, I had to learn to make lunch for myself. Charlotte took a picture of that first bacon sandwich. Dad brought home the *Romeo and Juliet* movie he'd watched in his schooldays. Lucas and I toiled through the hardest algebra questions and we slaved away making stop-motion films for media. But nothing could prepare me for English.

The school ran its lessons in sets, from the best-performing children to the lowest-performing. My cohort at Portum was placed in the bottom set for English. The teacher never stopped shouting; the students engaged in pencil-throwing wars.

Jordan always smiled in Portum, greeting everyone. He saw our classmates as his friends. The two boys behind him grinned, poking him and exploiting his naivety. Everyone else seemed preoccupied, avoiding pencils and trying to work. The moment you stepped inside that classroom, you were in the maelstrom.

Thunderous shouting, not a single window open, not a light on. My body became a sauna, heat-forged in fear. *Romeo and Juliet*, a battle between two households. The English classroom, a frightening fight for survival. Words, analysis, all a plunge into boredom. Unable to maintain control, the teacher always screamed and shouted at us.

In an effort to remedy the issues, they decided that halfway through the lesson, we'd be split off into two classes. The most well-behaved students went to Portum with my cohort, where Rosaline, a music teacher, desperately tried to deliver the curriculum. By that point, all I could see in *Romeo and Juliet* were putrid words on a page, containing nothing I found of substance.

I gave up the subject when Jordan burst into tears after being struck by pencil.

'Lucas, this is crap. We're leaving,' I said. He didn't disagree, breathing a sigh of relief.

***

«So, the fuckers just threw a pencil at him?» asked Bradford943.

«Yeah, I got the hell out of there,» I replied.

«Sorry you had to go through that.»

«I'm fine now, thanks. Not going to English again though.»

Galactic Conquest, my sanctuary at home, was all I had to live for. But even there I was trading one battleground for another. The Shadow Imperium had gained in strength. Occasionally one or two of them would attack our base, small provocations designed to unnerve us, trick us into becoming the aggressor. We saw right through their ploys; we didn't play into them. I hoped Draxx14 would come around and order them to stop. But it was hard to ignore the comments they made about us. «Don't take them seriously, they have a gay general. One of their commandos is dyslexic.»

«They're retarded.» «They have the aim of a toddler.» Such comments drove paranoia in my brain.

What if they attacked us while I was at school? While I was sleeping? They could destroy my hard work at any moment. I believed Diablous034 and Invicta11 were manipulating Draxx14.

Maybe I could win by showing him the truth. I didn't have any hard evidence, so I forged some, creating falsified screenshots of Diablous034 planning a coup. Surely Draxx14 would listen.

«My spies reported this,» I declared, my fingers trembling as I typed.

«You have spies in the Shadow Imperium?» he challenged me.

«No, we saw it in the Skype chat.»

«How did you get into our Skype chat?»

«We didn't, he posted it publicly.»

«I don't care how you got it, is it true or not?»

«Yes.»

He said nothing else. Just another failed plan as the Shadow Imperium crept closer. Under my leadership, the Paladins prepared for anything, everything. In the middle of a noisy classroom, I drafted battle plans in my head. Upon returning home, I instructed my forces in newly devised strategies.

«You're paranoid, it's not gonna be World War Three,» Bradford943 said. «They're cowards, they'll never fight us on our terms.»

«They've attacked with small squads,» I said.

«Yeah, to provoke us into attacking them. They know we can't win at their base.»

«Why not?»

«Have you seen the number of bunkers and barricades on those bridges? It's better we leave them alone; they'll move on, eventually.»

«I've never seen the Devil Dogs give up. They think they're pure warriors or some shit.»

«You and I know how guilds work. Eventually they'll be confronted with a greater threat, and they'll forget all about us. We're here to enjoy the game. You shouldn't be stressing over this.»

Bradford943 had a point, but as term dragged on the pressure increased. Our usual bus escort left, and the journeys became longer. Lessons became more repetitive, and my endurance continued to wane.

I tapped my feet, gaze fixated on my computer.

'Just consider going to English,' dad said. *After what happened to Jordan? No way.*

'OK, OK, fine.'

For most people, threats in the school corridors are invisible. For me, danger always rendered itself visible. At any moment, I could become entertainment for a pack of hungry year elevens. Balls, arms, legs, bags, they all crashed into me. Every second, I'd have to discern between hostile and non-hostile sounds. So Jayden and I formed a nonverbal agreement to watch each other's backs.

Without Lucas, Jayden or anyone else, I always had to be alert. On the journey to Portum, I had a choice of two stairs. One of them was wide with only two flights; the other was inside a courtyard, albeit narrower, with a slippery railing. A lot of Portum students favoured it, including me.

***

Fog blinded my vision; morning chills got under my coat. Before climbing the slender staircase, I peered behind me. *Nobody can attack you from behind, safe to go up.*

The door smashed open like an artillery barrage.

'I'll fucking do ya!' a boy roared.

I quaked, paralysed by an aura of fright. Two teenagers enthralled in animalistic instinct. Their voices unending war cries. Pulverising punches, riveting kicks, nuclear violence.

Caught in the middle of the stairs, I turned to flee. But in my path stood a girl, her eyes flashing with terror. We stood at the same height, but she seemed younger. *Follow me, follow me – come on, get the words out.* We stared at each other, unable to speak. *Can't just stand here, I'm sorry.* I dashed upstairs, braving the battle in front of me, narrowly avoiding an earth-shattering kick to the stomach. "Diary of Jane" by Breaking Benjamin playing in my head, music and adrenaline carried me up to Portum. I didn't stop until I reached the kitchen.

169

'Oh, that's quite an impressive run,' Charlotte commented. Shellshocked, I pretended not to hear her. *What if they had kicked me? Why couldn't I help her? I would have done it on Galactic Conquest. No, you made it out alive, don't be paranoid.* I only told Bradford943, nobody else would understand. The very thought of admitting vulnerability brought on an embarrassment that prevented me from ever vocalising my feelings. Though it hurt, I preferred to soldier on.

Chapter 15: Boiling

I dumped my bag in the hallway, but its weight still suffocated my shoulders.

'We're drafting your EHCP with the council. If you want to stay at Portum, you need five GCSES. That's it,' dad said. 'Why aren't you going to English?'

'It's shit,' I muttered. 'Imagine actually caring about Shakespeare.'

'Shakespeare was a genius, if you applied yourself—'

'Shakespeare is a wanker.'

'Fine, think whatever you want. It's about climbing the ladder, otherwise you can't stay at Portum.'

Easy for you to say. You're not the one in that classroom. 'OK, whatever, I'm going upstairs. Gonna train with my men.'

'Remember, we're going to see Naomi in an hour, your training isn't as important.'

'It will be when the Shadow Imperium tries to kill us.'

'Sorry, what did you say?'

'Nothing, forget it.'

English class was a screaming competition. I never returned after Jordan got hit with a pencil. But

'Mathematics makes you smarter,' so everyone told me. *Yeah, right, only idiots care about the value of B.* Exhausted within weeks, and with the Shadow Imperium at the door, I abandoned going to most lessons. I deemed the survival of my guild more important.

Arthur and Lucas had to negotiate if they wanted me to do any schoolwork.

'We'll do the rest of the work in Portum.'

'Go to Maths today and you won't need to go tomorrow.'

To keep Galactic Conquest a secret, I left the kitchen and went into the empty rooms available. There I'd coordinate the Paladins over Discord. (Playing the game itself would have people asking too many questions and thus finding out about my guild, so I never did.)

***

It's a Friday, Lucas is out at university. I sit alone, messaging my generals in the US about our new base. For them, school isn't due to start for another few hours. «If they try coming through the caves, we hide in the shadows and stab them,» I said.

«Might work,» one of my generals replied. «We've seen the Shadow Imperium aren't good in melee combat.»

«Exactly, so we use that to our advantage.»

Charlotte burst into the room. I spun around, skin tingling.

'Oh, I'm so sorry, did I startle you?' She asked. 'Someone needs to do a mock in here, would you...'

I groaned, leaving for the kitchen, laptop screen carefully concealed.

'You know, that's so kind and mature. I really appreciate it.'

«Sorry, teacher told me to move,' I typed. 'Let me just catch up with what everyone's said. I agree with encircling them.»

Charlotte had crept up behind me, as though she were approaching a stray kitten.

'Max, you have an English mock. You can either do it now or tomorrow. You can't just play games on your computer, we're in school,' she piped.

«Hold on, teacher's back. This one's super annoying.»

With a heavy sigh, I put my laptop on the table. 'I'm not playing games, this is more important than shitty *Romeo and Juliet.*'

'Please don't swear. You have two choices, either Maths revision or your English mock.'

'I'm not doing it, I'm busy. Leave me alone.'

'Busy with what, Max? You're in school, whatever you're doing can wait till you get home.'

'Fuck English, fuck Maths. Stop wasting my time. This is important.'

She snatched the laptop. 'I'm taking this because I think it's upsetting you.'

My jaw tightened, molten rage fuming. 'Give it back or I'm going to hurt you.'

'Not until you do your English mock. Well done for controlling your anger.'

'You can't con me into doing what you want.'

'I'm not trying to con you. I'm sorry you feel that way.' She handed my laptop to a teaching assistant. I attempted to pursue, only for Charlotte to block my path.

'Last chance. Give it back or I will hurt you.'

'Maybe you could hit a pillow or throw some balls around.'

The Shadow Imperium loomed, their armies ready to crush me. And an English mock is more important than preparing? Teeth gritted, I jolted to the kitchen drawers, rummaging for knives. 'Where are the knives, you fucking bitch? Afraid I'll stab you?'

Eyes wide, shoulders hunched, she held her ground. 'I removed them because I was worried you'd get angry.'

'You're the stupid cow who made me angry. It's your fault.' I grabbed a wooden spoon, lunging for her face. She held up her elbow, barely blocking it. I tried various weapons – scissors, pencils, a plastic compass. But she held firm. Fine, if I couldn't hurt her physically, I'd prey on her emotions.

Hand-crafted owls, plates, plants, all smashed. 'Get down on your knees, you fucking bitch.'

She sighed, eyes meeting the floor.

'I always hated it here. It's all shit, you just can't see it like I can.' I came closer, wielding another pair of scissors. 'Get on your knees, woman. Or I'll gut your fucking eyes out.'

She turned away, ignoring my vilifications. My throat trembled, every muscle ached. I looked around the ravaged kitchen, before resigning myself to sulking in a corner. Later, Arthur returned my laptop. Part of me wanted to apologise, but Charlotte and I didn't exchange another word, every action draining me.

***

'Are you alright?' grandma asked.

'I'm fine, let's just go home.'

'You can tell us if something's wrong. Baba and I love you very much.'

'Sheila, if something's wrong, he'll tell us,' grandpa said. 'Why don't we go to Costa? I'd like a hot chocolate.'

'A hot drink will do you good, Max. You look worn out, it must be all the hard work you're doing. We're all proud of you.' Guilt swarmed my lungs as though it were a clan of insects devouring a carcass. *I don't deserve this.*

'Sounds good. I had a difficult English exam.' *Why did you say that?* At home, mum and dad pressed

175

me for answers. I lied, telling them I didn't remember. If I confronted my actions openly, I believed the pain would get worse.

The start of half-term created distance between me and Charlotte, which was probably a relief to both of us. Online, I finished my new base. But when giving the opening speech to my men, pain tore a path through my mind. A dagger forged from the wildfire of my emotions. Later, during training, Bradford943 caught on. He sent me a private message on Discord. «What happened, you're not putting up much of a fight.»

«Some crap at school.»

«Clearly, it's just not any old crap at school, you never die that easily.»

«Charlotte wanted me to do an English mock, shitty *Romeo and Juliet*.» I explained what happened whilst someone else took over the training.

«Listen, you're lucky to have Portum. I would kill to get out of my GCSEs. Hell, if I did what you did, I'd get expelled and probably arrested.»

«We both know I'm not gonna pass my GCSEs. I can't last a second outside Portum.»

«GCSEs suck, school sucks. Don't think about the work you're doing, questioning it will drive you crazy.»

«Even if I do it. What happens when I run into the wrong person outside Portum?»

«Kick em in the balls and be done with it. Or pull the autism card.»

«The autism card?»

«Sorry, I don't wanna offend you or whatever, but when we had autistic kids here, they got away with a lot, and I'm sure you do too.»

«Your school had autistic kids. What happened to them?»

«They got bullied, parents got pissed. Now the school won't take any more.»

«Fair enough, and Portum students do get away with a lot, but no one will ever let me get away with this.»

«Listen, apologise to Charlotte, ask them to put you in another English class, and try not to think about the work you're doing.»

«What about the Shadow Imperium, can you handle things here? I don't wanna abandon you all.»

«They won't raid while we're at school. Besides, I spoke to Draxx, and he says they're not interested in us.»

«Why didn't Draxx just tell me?»

«He doesn't think you're a "true leader" or some crap. Don't send them any more fake screenshots, I'm sure they'll leave us alone soon.»

«I don't think ignoring them is working.»

«Diablous and Invicta are persistent twats. We both know they want us to attack them. They'll take advantage of your paranoia and it's all gonna end with you feeling worse, which is the last thing you need right now.»

«And if they attack us officially?»

«We'll beat them back, don't worry about us. Now, it's almost midnight, I suggest we get some sleep.»

«OK, thank you, Bradford.»

***

Lying in bed that night exposed me to further attack. I tried but was unable to sleep, my mental defences torn down with regret and fear. When I closed my eyes, I'd get caught in a never-ending fever dream: the Shadow Imperium over-running my guild, being expelled from school, never amounting to anything in life. All the images ran in a loop. I never slept.

Morning drew nearer and I couldn't lie there any longer. *It might stop if you eat something.* I went downstairs to the kitchen, barefoot under the gaze of sunrise. I turned on the lights and my senses abandoned me. Horrible, haunting images, a realm of dreaded fantasy. I saw Invicta11 and Diablous034 celebrating as they destroyed the Paladins. Pain swelled in my head as a group of teenagers threw me down the stairs at school. Susan's breath hovered in my nose, her laugh, her voice. *Grotty.* I opened my eyes, enduring the pounding in my head.

Minutes later I came out of the kitchen, dashing out and swearing under my breath. I had injured myself, on purpose. My parents saw the scar, but I lied about the cause. Fortunately, I found the strength to never harm myself again.

After a week, the scar healed and school started. I didn't apologise to Charlotte, guilt and embarrassment locked the words inside my head. I couldn't bring my laptop to school anymore, and my lesson attendance continued to worsen.

For all my life, I had tried to participate in academia, but it never brought me happiness or visible benefits. Galactic Conquest on the other hand did, and the Shadow Imperium wanted to destroy all I had built there. No more provocations, no more abuse, we were ready for war. An opportunity to start such a conflict came with a group of Devil Dogs veterans.

Not all of them supported Invicta11 and Diablous034. Some of them had created their own guild and directly opposed the Shadow Imperium. On a chilly Sunday morning, they reached out to me. Sakurhito, a well-respected Devil Dogs member abandoned his superiors in the Shadow Imperium to join the newly created opposition. He and some of his comrades were asking for my help in a surprise attack against our shared enemy.

If successful, we would destroy their capability to wage war in one fell swoop, I couldn't refuse. If Bradford943 had been there he'd have advised against it, but studying had taken up all of his time.

The Shadow Imperium base had two bridges leading into their main fortress. Inside stood Draxx14's throne room, where the capture point awaited. If Sakurhito was right, the need to manage real-life events had stopped the Shadow Imperium's best men from getting online. When we attacked, they'd be outnumbered and without proper leadership. The plan seemed perfect. We'd slowly move across the bridges, taking cover behind barricades. Then we'd rush for the throne room, destroying the tyrants and bringing them to the negotiating table. I hoped that Draxx14 would see Diablous034 and Invicta11 for who they were. Perhaps he would see me as a "true leader" and join us again.

Sakurhito introduced me to Robotics92, his leader. Because we enjoyed the same music, we got along right off the bat. Both of us, tired of the provocations and eager for vengeance, agreed to Sakurhito's plan. It was 10pm, November 26th, 2016. The song "Riot" by Three Days Grace acted as battle serum. Between us, we had twenty-five men.

We marched across the bridges but someone had removed the barricades. Without cover, we had no defence against the oncoming barrage. Invicta11 and Diablous034 joined with reinforcements, and the slaughter began. All my men charged into the meat grinder. We died like cattle whilst Shadow Imperium soldiers hid safe in their bunkers. Our bodies littered the bridge. A dizziness swelled in my eyes.

«Pathetic retards,» Invicta11 gloated. I turned off my music, laser fire drowning out my thoughts. Tears swelled in my eyes, I had failed my friends, my new allies, and myself.

Dad entered the room, 'Who's shooting? Are you winning?'

Finding me slumped over my desk in tears, he rushed over to hug me. The great XMA24, coddled, running away from battle. I didn't rally my men, I just turned off the computer and ran. *I'm a coward. I can't do anything right.*

Chapter 16: Exploding

«After you left, we just kept fighting,» a Paladin said. «We thought you had internet problems or something.»

«No, I didn't have internet problems. I led you all into a trap, they knew we were coming.»

«A trap, sir?»

«It's obvious, how else would they man the bunkers that quickly? How come the barricades disappeared over the course of an hour? I fucked up and I'm sorry.»

I'd given the Shadow Imperium an excuse for war. They'd descend upon our base, and I feared we weren't ready. *Maybe I should quit, give the guild to somebody else.* I entertained the thought, but I couldn't abandon my friends. Galactic Conquest was my life and giving up because of a bad defeat didn't feel right. I had to redeem myself. We might have lost a battle, but we hadn't lost the coming war. Nobody in the real world knew, nor would they "understand". No longer did I worry about a potential explosion. Now I feared the coming real explosion, a showdown that would decide the fate of my guild and countless others.

If the Devil Dogs returned under Draxx14, and those pulling his strings, the face of Galactic Conquest would change forever.

***

'So basically, X equals one,' Lucas sighed.

I nodded, staring out the window. *If they try flanking us we can—*

'Can you hear me?' He waved his hand in front of my face.

'Yes, but isn't X a letter? This is retarded.'

'I know it's boring, but like I told you, school is a training ground, we have to learn.'

'So you say.'

'Can we at least try five more questions? You're clever, it'll take you fifteen minutes.'

Images of our defeat, my friends falling victim to laser fire. 'Max, are you there?'

'Uh yeah, no, I won't do it.'

'Are you sure?'

I stood up to my full height. 'I'm not fucking doing it.'

Lucas groaned. 'Seriously, just five more—'

'No, it fucking sucks, it's pointless.'

Somehow, the atmosphere got warmer. For a while, neither of us said a word.

'Well, I don't know what to tell you Max. I can't force you to do it.'

'Just fuck off, Lucas. Alright? Just fuck off.' His jaw muscles grew tense, eyes unmoving. 'I've got shit to do.'

He grabbed me by the shoulders, frustration commanding his every movement. I stumbled back, bolting out the door.

'Max, wait. I'm sorry.'

An hour passed, I seethed in tears of rage. In the kitchen, Lucas was doing art with another student. I charged inside, grabbing a cutlery knife.

'Hey, if you touch him, I'm gonna mess you up,' the student threatened.

I pointed the knife towards his eyes. 'Fuck off!' He stood up, approaching me, fists raised.

'Brandon, don't worry about it. Sit down,' Lucas said.

'He better be careful, I'll beat him up next time.'

I circled around the table, with Brandon keeping a watchful eye. Lucas in range, knife in my shuddering hands. *He protected you.* We looked at each other, both unsure what to say or do. I poked his shirt with the knife but I couldn't hurt him. Something inside me wouldn't allow it.

I retreated, crying.

***

'Do you remember it?' dad asked.

'No,' I replied.

'What about trying to poison that boy's food?'

'I tried doing that?'

'You tried to add bleach to his drink.'

'Don't remember.'

I believed Brandon a threat to my safety. In a spur of anxiety surrounding him, I became machine-like, obsessed with one objective, a perceived need to protect myself. I knew it was wrong but couldn't control myself. Emotion had taken over and self-control proved impossible.

***

'Punch a pillow,' Charlotte said. 'It's important we're kind to each other in Portum.' *Someone wants to beat me up, and you're telling me to be kind? Punch a pillow? It never works.* If I couldn't access a computer, I'd pace the hallways, conjuring plans to defeat the Shadow Imperium.

Whilst Draxx14 stayed in the background, studying at university, Invicta11 and Diablous034 would come to our base and threaten us. «You don't know when, but we're coming.» They'd insult my friends, calling them things like «gay retard». When we retaliated, they would portray us and our allies as the aggressors.

At school, I became more anxious and increasingly frustrated. Rather than going to lessons, I spent my time on Discord, leading the Paladins from school. However, this didn't mean I could take part in every battle. I missed the Shadow Imperium's counterattack, which happened when I was on the bus. Invicta11 and Diablous034 led a large force of troops in an unprecedented effort to overwhelm our defences. When I returned, I found Bradford943 and our men celebrating a victory.

«How the hell did we win?» I pressed.

«Robotics brought reinforcements,» Bradford943 replied.

«But they still outnumbered us.»

«They did, so I led a small force behind their lines. They forgot to guard the capture point after taking it.»

«And they didn't have time to retake it?»

«No, but Invicta had time to accuse us of cheating.»

«Lol, what a twat!» I paused. «It's lucky you were off sick, or else we wouldn't be standing here.»

«You can't stop every attack, don't stress yourself out.»

«No, but if I didn't have school. I'd be able to fight with you.»

«Speaking of which, I have mocks to study for. I'm sorry, but you're gonna have to make do without me.»

«You'll be back during the holidays though, right?»

«Yes, just leave the Shadow Imperium alone. Everything will be fine.»

«Ignoring them hasn't worked.»

«It was working, but then you and Robotics attacked them. Now we're back at square one.»

«Draxx might do something if we explain it to him.»

«Don't bother with him, he's a lost cause.»

In victory we had wounded their pride, so Diablous034 and Invicta11 ramped up their harassment tactics. They spread vicious lies about us and tried numerous other forms of sabotage. Somehow, they found IMaginkI's portfolio site and sent him slanderous emails. Unable to win on the battlefield, they sought alternative means to ruin the game for us.

***

«I've told them not to do it,» Draxx14 said.

«Good, because we have their IP addresses. IMaginkI was about to call the police on them.»

«Only an idiot calls the police about mean things on the internet. Choose better generals.»

Once they realised IMaginkI could trace them, they stopped sending him emails. But the harassment continued, and Draxx14 refused to do anything about it. I spent most of my time on Galactic Conquest, trying to resolve the issues and save my guild. I'd blocked Diablous034 and Invicta11 on Discord, but that didn't stop them from creating new accounts to harass me and others. War came closer with each passing day, and trying to reason with Draxx14 was the definition of hitting my head against a brick wall. Without much sleep, I'd arrive at school tired and grumpy.

Portum was designed for students to attend classes in the mainstream school. But with my refusal to do anything but Galactic Conquest, it became a glorified babysitting service. *What's the point of being here? The Paladins need me at home.* I removed the batteries from my parents' alarm clocks, so they wouldn't get up to wake me. I fantasised about blowing up the school with fireworks. At the same time, the fun had been slowly sucked out of Galactic Conquest. My life had become a downward spiral of torment and stress, with no end in sight. Charlotte permitted me to bring my laptop back into Portum; she and my parents hoped it would quell further meltdowns. For lunch, I'd tell Lucas what I wanted and he'd get it for me.

Everyday I faced a battle, both in the real world and online. Not wanting to appear "weak", I put on a façade of happiness. After all, nobody would understand the Shadow Imperium or why I feared traversing the school; they'd probably just find it silly. Trapped between the beginnings of puberty and everything else, life had never seemed more hopeless.

I tried to find escapism in other games. With Bradford943 revising for his mock exams, I left my generals in charge of the Paladins. I was finishing off a cellblock in Prison Architect when suddenly my stomach trembled with paranoia. *I'll just check, I'm sure everything's fine.*

I closed my game and checked Discord. My chest tightened, a shiver struck me like a bullet. Our server stood in ruins, all the text channels had been filled with pornographic imagery and violent gore. I closed my eyes and opened the announcements to discover that one of my generals had betrayed me. He'd posted the following message:

12.12.16

«HAIL THE SHADOW IMPERIUM! HAIL DRAXX14! WE ARE SUPERIOR OUR LEADER DRAXX HAS SENT HIS ELITE HAXORS ON YOU.» I swiftly banned him, without a second thought.

«So what the fuck happened?» Draxx14 asked.

«You did this, stop fucking lying,» a Paladin shot back accusingly.

«Vish, people know the Paladins and the Shadow Imperium haven't had good relations recently. Someone could have done this to start a war, and you're doing what they want right now. Use your brain for once.»

«Bullshit.»

«I didn't order this or cause this. I'm a friend of XMA and I'm trying to help.» My throat twisted. *I'm fucked, it's the end.*

«XMA, come to the Shadow Imperium's base. I have an offer for you.»

The Paladins was close to one-thousand members, and now a traitor had kicked two hundred from the guild. Crudely drawn penises littered our base. Our entire organisation had been hurled into the fires of chaos, all my hard work destroyed in less than half an hour. Once I'd patched up the damage, I made my way to the Shadow Imperium's base, where Draxx14 awaited atop his throne. His unquestioning soldiers guarded him, their weapons pointed at me. They were the perfect dogs of war. Once I had stood side by side with Draxx14, now I quavered at his mercy.

«You're not a true leader, you never should have left me,» Draxx14 began. «Look around, all my men respect me. They give me the loyalty you'll never have.»

«Why did you abandon your brothers then?» I challenged.

«What brothers? I never abandoned anyone.»

«Me, Bradford, and everyone else, you replaced us.»

One of his guards fired a warning shot. *Shouldn't have said that.*

«I did it to keep the Shadow Imperium alive. A good leader knows when to make reforms.» An eerie silence hung in the air, two guards moved to block the exit. «I'm going to offer you a choice. You will either accept it or the Paladins will fall because of your poor leadership.»

«What does your offer entail?»

«The Paladins will merge into the Shadow Imperium. You'll help us destroy Robotics92, and in exchange I'll make you the same rank as Invicta and Diablous.»

I wanted to fight with Draxx14 again, I wanted an end to the chaos. But I couldn't betray Robotics92. He'd helped us fight off the Shadow Imperium, and he was my friend.

Besides, Draxx14 had no reason to keep his word. If he wanted to, he could just demote me again. «We'll become the most powerful guild in the game,» Draxx14 enticed. «Our brotherhood will be reformed, isn't that what you want?»

«I'm going to turn that down. My guild needs me,» I replied.

«I urge you to reconsider. You're not fit to be a true leader.»

With teary eyes I endured his barrage. «Sorry, but I think we're done here.» I trudged over to the exit. «Excuse me.»

At Draxx14's command, the guards let me go. Later, after somewhat stabilising the Paladins, I confronted the general who'd betrayed me.

«I'm sorry, XMA. My family doesn't have a lot of money.» He said that attached with a screenshot. Someone named "Darren Wilson" had given him forty pounds to destroy the Paladins. Darren was Draxx14's real name, he'd done this.

«Fuck off and never speak to me again,» I cursed. Everything matched up perfectly, the Shadow Imperium couldn't beat me and Robotics92 together, so one of us had to be taken out. And recently Draxx14 had got a job as a fry cook, meaning he was the only one with the money to bribe one of my generals.

Whenever I pieced the jigsaw together, I'd be overwhelmed by a wave of sorrow. Why would Draxx14 betray me? We were friends, we fought together. I didn't want to believe it, so I lied to myself. *Diablous and Invicta just manipulated him, he'll come around and apologise. Eventually.* Had I not checked Discord in time, I would have lost everything.

Fearful of the same thing happening to his guild, Robotics92 placed everyone on high alert. Sakurhito launched an investigation of his own, insisting a "third party" had done it and not Draxx14. I was suspicious but didn't have time to chase it up. The Paladins had been devastated; I spent all my time desperately trying to repair the damage. We weren't able to wage war, that's what the Shadow Imperium wanted. Without us, Robotics92 couldn't defeat them, which meant the coming conflict would be laughably one-sided. Both sides harboured a mountain of resentment, leading to progressively larger skirmishes.

I didn't want to antagonise Draxx14, but the battles were unavoidable. Perhaps naively, I still believed negotiation with him was possible.

***

«Word of advice, shits going down between Robotics and The Shadow Imperium. If you want the Paladins to survive, stay out of it,» Draxx14 threatened.

Dread twisted in my gut. I scanned the kitchen to make sure nobody was watching. «Why have you declared war?» I asked. «Robotics didn't tell me anything.»

«I didn't declare war, you're the aggressors.»

«Robotics wouldn't go to war without consulting me.»

«I have proof, hold on.» After a few seconds, he sent a screenshot. «Undeniable proof, choose your next words carefully.»

He'd sent me the conversation he'd had with Robotics92, though notably some of it had been cut.

«Where's the rest?»

«You don't need to see the rest.»

«Why did you insult him and his men?»

«Their existence is an insult to the legacy of the Devil Dogs. It's not my fault if he's sensitive and can't take criticism.»

My hands trembled as I typed. «Can I see the whole conversation?»

«No. You get one chance to back off or I'll have to destroy you.» He stopped responding after that. Fear choked my throat; we weren't ready for war with the Shadow Imperium. I decided it best to probe Robotics92 for information. I wanted the full picture before making my next move. Unfortunately, he lived in the US, so I'd have to wait hours for a reply.

I spent my school day in apprehension, unable to do anything significant as things exploded online.

***

«So, you declared war in the heat of the moment?» I asked.

«Yeah, he was talking smack about my girlfriend,» Robotics92 replied. «I'm not backing down; we can't let them be the ones to continue the Devil Dogs.»

I decided my best chance was to negotiate a peace treaty; that way we could buy time to rebuild. But alas, that meant convincing everyone to lay down their arms, including Draxx14. December 21st, the last day of school, I'd just embarked on a seemingly impossible journey.

***

'Max, you know Arthur is leaving, right? It's his last day here." Lucas hinted.

'Uh-huh. I'll see him later,' I half-heartedly replied, focused on my conversation with Draxx14.

Lucas shrugged. 'Alright then. But it's a half-day, so you'll have to see him soon.'

***

«Invicta is more human than you. He is strong-willed and violent when you insult him or what he believes in.»

«Can't you see he's using you?» I pressed.

«He's loyal and truthful, and I'd rather have him at my side than you, XMA. You've become very big headed

194

since you left the Shadow Imperium, and it's hard to be respectful towards you now.» Draxx14 paused before typing his next message. «The Paladins isn't the amazing guild you like to think it is. I know the Shadow Imperium isn't perfect but it's improving. Something you've stopped doing – pushing forward and improving.»

«Maybe the Paladins isn't perfect either, but we're trying to negotiate here.»

«I don't care, stop trying to be a jedi or some shit. Now if you don't mind, I'm going to surprise my girlfriend with a visit. Goodbye.»

He went offline, leaving me no chance to respond. *OK, you're more successful than me, stop rubbing it in. Fuck, what am I even gonna do here? They've already won.*

I looked at the time on my laptop, just a few minutes past twelve. In roughly twenty minutes the school term would be over. Had I been conversing with Draxx14 all that time? I stood up, clutching the laptop under my arm. Perhaps it wasn't too late to say goodbye to Arthur.

The other students gave him a testosterone-filled farewell. I watched from a distance, as everything in my body screamed for me to leave. *I'll come back when it's less crowded.* I scurried to the kitchen. The world rushed by in a blur, then both my body and laptop tumbled to the floor. Bruised knees and a cracked device that wouldn't turn on. *Maybe Draxx is right, I'm not a good leader, can't even take care of my laptop.* I hid it inside its case; hopefully mum and dad wouldn't notice.

'Max, its home-time,' Lucas called.

'Really?'

He smiled, 'Yep, you can finally catch up with your video games.'

'Yeah, I-I guess I can.'

If I hadn't seen Arthur on the way out, I wouldn't have been able to say goodbye. Christmas and the end of term weren't something to celebrate: a well-loved teaching assistant had left Portum, and I had to negotiate an impossible peace. But through calling in favours, pulling strings and making the right concessions, I did it.

TREATY BETWEEN THE SHADOW IMPERIUM
AND ROBOTICS92's DEVIL DOGS
DECEMBER 23RD, 2016

By order of the Supreme Chancellor of the Shadow Imperium and the Supreme Commander of the Devil Dogs, hostilities will cease. The war was set in motion by the Shadow Imperium for the purpose of suppressing the Devil Dogs' desire to continue the legacy of their original incarnation.

The Devil Dogs understands that the Shadow Imperium does not want the legacy continued, and therefore the

Devil Dogs will continue as its own guild. The guild will not function as a Devil Dogs legacy, but as a guild that coincidentally has the same name. On the terms of this treaty, both groups will end hostilities with the other, specifically in events such as: raids, disrespectful propaganda, alternate account raids, etc.

The Shadow Imperium will not host events such as those. Both guilds understand the war was a waste of time and resources, and from this moment forward there will be no conflicts between the two.

Signed,

Draxx14, Supreme Commander, the Shadow Imperium
Diablous034, Supreme Chancellor, the Shadow Imperium
Invicta11, Senior General, the Shadow Imperium

Robotics92, Supreme Commander, Devil Dogs
Sakurhito, General, Devil Dogs
XMA24, Supreme Leader, the Paladins

In three days, I'd ended a war. A ceasefire with nobody's guild destroyed, that's what I wanted, right? Though our guilds were safe, the Shadow Imperium had undeniably succeeded. Robotics92 had had his base reduced to rubble, and the Paladins' was still in chaos. Exhausted and drained of hope, I fully expected us to collapse.

***

«Guess I missed the shitshow, » said Bradford943. «Why are you online? It's New Year's Eve.»

«I fucked up, just trying to put things back together.»

«That's a bit of an understatement, but congratulations on the peace treaty.»

«I didn't just fuck up here, Arthur left but I was too busy with Draxx14's bullshit to properly say goodbye.» I slouched in my chair as waves of painful memories struck, each one a pulverising punch to the gut. «Let's face it, I'm a failure.»

«You made shitty mistakes, but beating yourself up won't change that.»

«Do you think I should just quit? You can lead the Paladins.»

«No, but you should take a break. It'll give you time to think about your fuckups.»

«Can you handle things here?»

«I'm with my family, and that's where you should be. Watch the fireworks with your folks or something. We'll start fixing things when you have a clear head.»

«Sounds good. Guess I need to play some games in peace right now. Thank you, we'll talk soon.»

Confidence had abandoned me, but Bradford943 was right. I'd made my mistakes, and self-loathing wouldn't change that.

Chapter 17: "Grow Up"

In the new year, I tried to relax by playing other video games. But one thing stayed in my head, like an annoying wrinkle on a duvet. One particular line of the treaty I'd painstakingly negotiated. Maybe you noticed it too: "*The war was set in motion by the Shadow Imperium.*"

The Shadow Imperium wanted to continue the legacy of the Devil Dogs themselves. Robotics92 opposing them with his own faction and allying with me gave them reason to declare war. Why wouldn't an army seize the chance to crush its greatest enemies in one fell swoop? It was the obvious course of action, except for the fact that they didn't declare war; Robotics92 did. "*The war was set in motion by The Shadow Imperium.*" With renewed clarity, I examined the treaty and connected the pieces together. Diablous034 had made a mistake in including that line. The ecstasy of victory had blinded him.

The Shadow Imperium had sought a war in which they would have the advantage. Through manipulation they'd created one, and we had walked right into it. Suddenly it all made sense. Draxx14 had the power to bribe my general at any time, but he did it days before the war began.

Without the Paladins, it would have been an easy victory for the Shadow Imperium.

But easy wasn't enough, Draxx14 wanted guaranteed victory. In provoking a declaration of war from Robotics92, he painted us as the aggressors and won a propaganda victory. So why did Draxx14 make peace? He could easily have finished us. There were two reasons. One, that he wanted me to merge into the Shadow Imperium. If he outright destroyed the Paladins, I would have been bitter and therefore less likely to agree . The second reason was that both our guilds – the Paladins and the Devil Dogs veterans – were in a mess. The Shadow Imperium could safely assume we would collapse on our own. But to them instant gratification was better than a prolonged conflict. And it doesn't end there. Days after we signed the treaty, Sakurhito left for the Shadow Imperium.

Throughout the war, our messages were leaked. Messages Sakurhito had access to. Suspiciously, Invicta11 was the one who posted the leaks, even though he wasn't in the same chat. Sakurhito also tried to divert our attention when Draxx14 bribed my general and neutralised the Paladins. When pressed for answers, Sakurhito ignored us. All logic dictated that he was a mole.

I got so caught up in fear and the desire to protect my guild. In doing so, I had played right into the Shadow Imperium's hands. I'd enabled their grand design and trampled on my real-world relationships and my mental health. My mistakes were visible; I could see them clearly, but it was too little too late.

***

«Are you familiar with the Franco-British union proposal?» I asked.

«No,» Robotics92 replied.

«When France fell in World War Two, the British proposed a union. But it wasn't concrete, and few wanted it.»

«We haven't fallen though. At least not yet.»

«We're close though; a lot of our men have left for other guilds. But if we combine our assets, at least until we defeat the Shadow Imperium, then we'll have a better chance of survival.»

«What if my men disagree?»

«The ones who stayed are loyal to you. Trust me, all of you should join the Paladins. We'll make it work.»

«Got nothing to lose, I'll do it.»

«Great, now let me tell you about our new base.»

I hadn't started studying for my GCSEs, and time was running out. At the end of year eleven, I'd need to leave Portum. Deep down, I didn't want to be stuck at home forever, but at this point it seemed inevitable. Even if I abandoned Galactic Conquest and poured myself into academia, I wouldn't succeed long-term.

The Paladins were my proudest achievement, I'd made so many friends there. All the surrounding adults would be jubilant if I abandoned them, but I'd feel empty. Doing my GCSEs and A-Levels would delay the inevitable: leaving Portum. At that point, I'd get thrown toward university, the first step towards becoming an independent adult. GCSEs and A-Levels are impressive, but they can't teach you all the skills needed to survive in the real-world. For years, I'd spent the day in my room; I didn't even know what a toilet brush was. GCSEs or not, I'd still be stuck at home, unable to cope with university. And there wasn't much time left to mature and learn the skills I lacked. How would I ever start with independence? At this point, academia seemed impossible to catch up on. I knew that Galactic Conquest wouldn't last forever. Eternal childhood is unrealistic and unfulfilling. These thoughts lurked in my subconscious, but I wasn't emotionally mature enough to confront them.

I decided I would stay the course with Galactic Conquest, at least until I defeated the Shadow Imperium. I'd work out the rest later, "at the right time", or so I liked to think of it.

***

'Fifteen minutes in the snow for Costa Coffee. The bakeries on the high street looked nice. I'm sure you'd put on more weight there,' Lucas hinted.

'It's not snowing, it's sleeting. There's a difference,' I countered.

'It never snowed back home.'

'Do you miss it?'

'Sometimes, but I don't regret studying here. I just got my internship.'

I peered out the window, watching the people outside fight their way through the sleet. 'You didn't tell me you got the job.'

'I don't have the job yet. But if I impress them, they might hire me.' *First Arthur and now you.* 'Max, are you alright? You're spacing out there.'

'Oh, sorry.' I took a sip of my hot chocolate.

'Did you get lost in your thoughts again?'

'Yeah, congratulations. It's what you've always wanted to do.'

'Aw, thank you, Max. I just hope I get the job.'

'You will. They'd be mad not to hire you.'

He sighed. 'If they hire me, I'll have to leave Portum.'

'I'm aware of that.'

'But I'll really miss you guys – if I get the job.'

'You already have it. I've seen your work.'

A smile adorned his face. 'Would you mind giving me constructive criticism?'

'Whenever you want.'

All those times he'd read my stories, the laughs we'd shared, the friendship we'd forged. When I was younger, I thought our time together would never end. Now, I'd begun to realise that the world isn't Neverland. Lucas couldn't stay at Portum, and I couldn't stay in Galactic Conquest.

Recently, at the feeding clinic, they'd confirmed I'd started puberty. Months earlier, they were ready to pull out the drugs. Some people didn't think it would happen, but I'd put on enough weight to transcend boyhood. Things were changing, Arthur had left, and now it seemed Lucas would follow.

However, if I wanted to steer the ship towards becoming an independent adult, I'd need to make important decisions soon. So many of my peers were already condemned to staying at home. How could I avoid that fate? Where or how could I begin?

Unable to make a choice, I stayed the course. The Paladins needed rebuilding, and I had my OT sessions to attend. In that time, I developed and learnt important skills with the help of those around me. I wasn't obligated to attend lessons anymore; I spent more time with Jayden, with Lucas, and with other TAs I grew close to.

I'd recovered from last year's explosive events but time hadn't stopped ticking. My ship was still on a collision course with an iceberg.

***

February 1st, 2017, it's late evening, I'm patrolling the vast orange sands with the Paladins. Suddenly, I receive a message from Draxx14.

«I'm coming to raid. Don't worry, when I win, I'll give your base back,» he said.

I didn't believe him for a moment. This was the Shadow Imperium striking the death blow, not a friendly game between friends. In-game, I stopped moving, hands trembling at the keyboard.

«Sir? Is everything alright?» One of my men asked.

«No, the Shadow Imperium is going to raid us. We'll be outnumbered.»

«We've beaten them before.»

«There's seven of us, and twenty of them. We're fucked.»

«So, we're just going to give them our base?»

«No, stand in shoulder-to-shoulder formation.»

Without questioning the order, my men formed a perfect line of six. A chill penetrated my bones. Was this the end of the Paladins?

«Chances are, we've already lost.»

I opened Spotify, started my "battle playlist" and turned up the volume.   «Honestly, I don't know where I'm going with this. But it's the best I have.»

«Permission to speak, sir?»

«Granted.»

«Whatever the plan is, we'll give those bastards hell.»

I smirked. «Listen closely, it's a big desert, they'll be exposed, and the capture point is on the mountain. We have the high ground. Hold it long enough for reinforcements to arrive, and we might pull this off.»

«Understood, sir, I've messaged everyone on Discord. If they're online, we'll have our reinforcements.»

«Good. Vish, Wizard, I want both of you in sniper positions. The rest of us will hold on the mountain. Let's move.»

It was as bad as I'd feared. Besieged by laser fire, we died one by one until, within minutes, I was the only one left.

«I thought you'd do better, XMA,» Draxx14 goaded. He and one of his guards drew closer with every step. «This is why you should merge. You'd be stronger with me.» I waited at the capture point with my mini-gun, the last man standing. "Not Gonna Die" by Skillet played in the background, acting as battle serum.

The air was sucked out and replaced with adrenaline. My sweat-soaked finger rested on the mouse button. When Draxx14 and his guard came into firing range, I unloaded deathly torrents of laser fire. Moments later, their corpses lay at my feet. Breathless, I found my thoughts empty. Then a Shadow Imperium soldier charged my position. *Fuck, I didn't look right.* A well-aimed sniper shot penetrated his skull. I peered up, finding Bradford943 saluting me. He'd arrived, bringing reinforcements with him. Inch by inch, we forced the Shadow Imperium back across the desert.

«A shame you can only win by cheating XMA,» Draxx14 shouted. Standing amidst the devastation of a bloodied battlefield, a numbness plagued my limbs. *Holy shit. I... we won.*

***

«He hacked the game, the Paladins are a trash guild,» Invicta11 said in scorn. «It's the only explanation.»

«Or you're all just shit players,» Bradford943 rebutted.

Draxx14 spent all night trying to defame our reputation. Without hard evidence, nobody believed him. Vindication was as sweet and as welcome as an oasis in a desert, but the war wasn't over. I wanted to see the Shadow Imperium in tatters. My empire was growing. Why descend into the stresses of schoolwork? No, I still wasn't "ready".

***

'So potentially if France had carried on with their offensive, World War Two might've ended much quicker,' I speculated.

'You'd be good in class. I'm sure the teacher would love your thoughts,' said grandma, complimenting me.

'I'm not doing history for GCSE. Besides, they don't care about discussion, it's all about conforming to a mark scheme.'

'Why don't you talk to Charlotte?'

I grimaced, remembering how I'd hurt Charlotte in my outbursts the year before.

'Max, are you alright?'

'I'm fine, just thinking. She can't change the exams. Even if a subject sounds interesting, it's just about appeasing the mark scheme.'

'So think outside of the box. Answer the questions in your own way. You can make it interesting.'

'I wish it were that simple. You either get the mark or you don't, it doesn't matter how you answer.'

'Baba and I think you're highly intelligent. You can find an exciting way of doing it. Talk to Lucas, he wants to help you.'

'Trust me, you can't make school exciting. It's always the same.'

'What about in class? Why don't you make some friends?'

'I got Jayden, I'll be fine. Besides, you don't wanna know what happens in English.'

'In the classroom?'

'Never mind.'

***

Lucas and I sat in the kitchen, deep in conversation

'You haven't watched the clone wars series yet, have you?' I asked.

'I don't have much time. I'm so busy with the internship.'

'Watch the Umbara arc when you can. It's a good—'

'You two look like you're having such a wonderful conversation,' Charlotte beamed. We stared back in silence. 'Am I interrupting anything?'

'No,' Lucas replied. 'Please join us.' A thick silence settled over us. Uneasy glances replaced the rhythmic tempo of the prior conversation. 'Uh, Max, do you want to say hello to Charlotte?'

'Um, hello.'

'I just saw you two talking. I really didn't want to interrupt. You were having such a pleasant chat.'

'Bit late now,' I muttered.

'I have a few questions to ask if that's OK.'

'Are you asking me or Lucas?'

'I mostly have questions for you.'

'Right, OK then.'

'Would you like to come to our social next Tuesday?' she asked. 'It's at the start of autism awareness week. You know, it would be fantastic if you came.'

'Oh, um, I'm doing something that night.'

'Will you be on the internet? On that game your dad was telling me about? Sorry, I can't remember what it's called.' *Do you need to bring it up?*

'Yes, something like that.'

'Right, well, I'll be happy to see your parents then.' Her gaze drifted to Lucas. 'I was just wondering if you could make something for our autism-awareness sale?'

'Yes. Max, can you get your mum to make a cake?'

'Yeah, sure.'

'Right, this all sounds fantastic. Enjoy your Costa coffee, you two.' With those words, Charlotte sauntered away.

'What if we did bookmarks?' Lucas suggested. 'You can do pixel art for them.'

'I'm not that good at art.'

'People won't mind, it's raising money for Portum.'

'I suggest we get Jayden to help. He's better at this than me.'

The bookmarks were a collaborative effort between four people. Lucas, me, Jayden, and Jayden's TA Sophie. I drew pixel art of cupcakes and coloured them all differently. The common theme was appeasing Charlotte, who wanted "difference shown positively". Each bookmark had a quote under it, reinforcing the ideology of Portum. This was my idea.

'They sold better than the cakes,' Charlotte jubilantly told us. I was proud to have helped raise money for Portum, though for some reason, I found it embarrassing to admit it.

***

«They'll destroy us if we don't merge,» Draxx14 pressed.

«Who? Sorry, but you haven't given me any evidence,» I replied. «I can't find anything on this guild's existence.»

«Are you really gonna just sit there? I don't know about you, but I'd rather die fighting than hide in a corner.»

'Max, are you going to bed soon?' dad called.

'In a minute, I'm typing something.' Caught in the turbulence of an icy conversation, I couldn't pull myself away. «I haven't seen the threat. Besides, if they're that threatening, every guild would scream about them.»

«By the time people learn it will be too late,» Draxx14 snapped. «I want this war while they're still establishing. Stop being a pussy and be a damn leader. Grow a pair of balls and stand up for your men. Or you have no right to lead.»

He was cutting deep now, far and hard. In internet arguments, there is a seldom spoken rule. Whoever gets the last word in "wins". I still harboured this mentality and didn't want my pride to be wounded.

«Listen, I'll offer an alliance but you need to show me some proof.»

«What help is that? I've defended you since day fucking one. I ask for your help, and for you and your men to come home. And this is what I get?»

«I'm sorry, but I will not merge with you. You'll probably be angry with me for saying this, but the answer will always be no.»

«You're making a mistake.»

«I'm tired, and I don't want to argue with you. Galactic Conquest doesn't control my life. Good night.»

«I came to a friend for help and I got a lump of fucking stone who doesn't listen. Thanks for killing off the ONLY CHANCE EITHER OF OUR GODDAMN GUILDS HAD! Enjoy dying, I'll die on the battlefield. You can die in your lazy-ass bed.»

Venomous words, a brutal assault on my soul. *He's taking this game too seriously.* I prepared to type another message. *It's not worth it. Go to bed.* Summoning every ounce of self-discipline, I tore myself away from the screen, pressing the power button before I had the chance to read any more of Draxx14's messages. But that didn't end the emotions surrounding the incident, as many thoughts swirled in my head that night.

Was I a coward for abandoning the argument? What if the threat he described was real, and not just a means to manipulate me? Were we so different? Both of us wrapped our causes in zeal, determined to fight and immortalise our names. And what about my legacy?

One day Galactic Conquest would end, and I'd need to grow up.

Chapter 18: The Pendulum Swings

'Max, come downstairs please,' dad called.

'Is something wrong?' I asked.

'Just come down.'

Disorganised paperwork lay scattered on the dining-room table. Mum bit her lip, slowly turning to dad.

'Charlotte has told us you need to leave after year eleven,' he lamented. 'She's told us to look for other places.' My heart plummeted a million feet down. *So much for celebrating difference.*

'The problem is there aren't many,' mum added. 'You might have to stay at home.'

'It's his decision, Lucy.'

'What are my choices?'

'A mainstream college or the school Naomi works at...'

'We can't afford that,' mum interjected. 'And the council won't fund it.'

'I've already got the prospectus. Naomi will get him a taster day.'

The conversation descended into anxiety. Neither of them could come up with another option for my future.

'I'll read the prospectus,' I announced, putting an end to their chatter. 'I'm going back upstairs.' Being removed from Portum was once a dark fantasy. Now I faced the choice of an inflexible college I'd never survive in or becoming a lost soul at home.

'Oh, it's good to be different,' I muttered. 'Just remember to become a GCSE slave. If you don't, we'll have to throw you out. Practice what you preach, Charlotte... fucking hypocrite.'

Through not attending lessons, I'd sealed my fate. I read the prospectus for Naomi's school in bed that night. It was a private school, Oakwood. They had an emphasis on life skills, on learning what I lacked. But it seemed a distant dream, and I hadn't visited yet. I didn't want to place all bets on a far-off placement, nor did I feel ready to steer the ship.

***

'Charlotte saw the Oakwood prospectus,' dad said.

'What did she say?' I asked.

'She said it's exactly what they'd like to offer, given more flexibility.'

'It's about the money then.'

'And what the school will allow. I'm sure she wants to keep all the kids, but it isn't always up to her.'

***

A dark corridor in White Mountain School, green smoke spewed from the walls. A man, tall and muscular, blocked the only exit.

'Where is Susan?' I asked.

His phantom eyes formed a piercing glare. 'You don't want to know.'

Windows, all decrepit. I charged towards one, leaping out. Darkness followed, my plummet seemed deliberately slow. Morning light seeped through the curtains, sweat had drenched my pyjamas. Another dream about primary school. In recent months, they had grown less frequent. But having to leave Portum had reawakened the trauma.

I feared another situation like my later years in White Mountain School. Any educational placement held that possibility.

***

24.4.17

Dear Charlotte,

Hope you had a lovely Easter break. We are enclosing some documents for Max's upcoming annual review. We've also included last year's report, to show how his situation has changed since then. Our meeting is on Monday 15th May, 2017 at 2pm. His paediatrician will attend, she's known him since the age of three.

We haven't heard from his EHCP caseworker, but hopefully she will also attend. Today Max will give you an ABAS-3 form that his OT and sensory integration physiotherapist, Naomi, would like you to fill in. To be honest, Charlotte, Lucy and I were devastated after spending time with you at the Portum social event.

Given Max's reluctance to work towards his GCSEs, and how budget cuts are affecting Portum, you're right in saying there is very little Crown Heights can offer him beyond July 2018, other than a "safe place". Your last email said it all when you told us that the Oakwood prospectus looked EXACTLY what Portum would like to offer, if you had more flexibility. Alas, the system is against you and us. But unfortunately, it's the children like Max who suffer most.

Looking for a way forward. Hopefully, our discussions at this year's annual review will give Max something to achieve in his last year at Portum. We are now faced with the impossible task of deciding for Max in September 2018. He will have just turned sixteen years of age, and our greatest fear is that he'll have nowhere to go.

Below are some thoughts from Lucy and I. We believe that going over old ground will help us move forward. What happened to Max last autumn shocked us all, and my search for an answer has led me to the timetable Lucas drew up on September 5th, 2016. It looks reasonable, five GCSES with space in between to revise and eat lunch.

On Friday the 21st of October, Max had a meltdown when you asked him to undertake an English mock exam. You handled the matter really well, but you were shocked at his language and how angry he became. Max couldn't remember when we asked him. How could he? Cortisone ran riot and flooded his hippocampus.

We have lived with Max's meltdowns for years, and over the last few he's become better at controlling himself. However, Max is complicated, and his PDA is always bubbling beneath the surface. Were his meltdowns caused by the pressure from a demanding routine of classes and GCSEs? Or was it the start of puberty? We can't peer into his brain, but we can assume all the stress overwhelmed him.

There is so much fear in Max still. The other week when we went to his feeding clinic and had lunch at a Carluccio's restaurant, I asked Max if I could go to the toilet, but he wouldn't let me leave him alone at the table. To feel safe, he had to accompany me. It's a similar situation when leaving the house. He has to wear his coat and hood.

As for attending a class of 35 noisy and playful kids. Forget it, his fear and sensory difficulties won't allow that. This isn't an anxiety to be treated with drugs. Only through exposure and maturity will he improve. For him, showers are still intolerable, and cutting his food or brushing his teeth without help is impossible.

So where do we go from here? Let's start with the positives. Max continues to work with Naomi and she states that in the past 18 months he has made remarkable progress. She says his OT/sensory needs are complex, but with the right working approach she sees great potential. They work so well together.

He has also started puberty and is growing. (Though he's still underweight for his age.)

His speech on his mother's birthday was awe-inspiring. He enjoys going to Portum and likes the people there. Overall, we are seeing the beginnings of a wonderful young man. Max has come far, but still needs support. How do we at least coax him into achieving a positive outcome at the end of year 11?

Maybe we can guide him towards at least one GCSE. He's good with computers, types fast, and his latest story is about a dystopian world. So I'm sure we can find something for him to achieve. I've looked at our options. Boarding school and residential are out of the question for Max. And since he cannot stay at Portum, we feel that the best option is Oakwood. Naomi works there, so hopefully they'll have a sixth-form place for him.

As Max grows older, and matures, he will be in a better place to achieve his potential. For now, he just needs time and a safe space to grow. Thank you, Charlotte, for listening to our concerns and for your continued support. I also have sent this email to Max. Him reading it is part of the process.

Regards

Nick and Lucy Toper

The email held truths that I had tried to ignore for years. Confrontation was painful, and I lacked the emotional resilience to vocalise my feelings. I didn't understand why I wore a coat and hood. I'd simply put it on one day and hadn't had the confidence to take it off again. Many things were unclear, and I couldn't envision a bright future. But if there was a button to fix my sensory issues, I would certainly have pressed it.

***

'Max are you alright?' Lucas asked.

'Did you get the email my dad sent? He's trying to make me do GCSEs again.'

'I didn't get the email, but it's still your choice. We can't make you do anything.'

'I'll send it to you.'

'Why do you want me to read it?'

'I-I don't know... I'll just send it anyway.' He read it twice, taking everything in. 'What do you think?'

'I think you can do GCSEs, but like I said it's up to you.'

'Yep, guess so.'

'Shall we go to Costa Coffee and have some breakfast?'

'Yeah, sure.' I peered out the door. Some older boys were blocking the steps. 'We'll wait till they move.'

'They'll move if we ask. Come on.'

'OK.'

I didn't dare leave Lucas's side, not until we left school. Once we arrived in Costa Coffee, he had to order for me. We sat down in a corner, out of everyone's way.

'How well is Portum funded?' I asked.

'I'm not sure. You can ask Charlotte, but I don't think she can tell you.'

'What about the budget cuts? Do they affect Portum, is that why she can't tell us?'

'It's a shame about the budget, but I don't know anything. Sorry.'

'Even if it isn't affecting us now, it will eventually. What will we do then?'

Lucas sighed, his hands placed on his knees. 'I really don't know, Max. But you're right, it will affect us at some point. And when it does, I'm sure Charlotte will handle it.'

She already is, by throwing out the terrible students like me. The system just wants more GCSE slaves. But what if my negligence had affected Portum? Was I partially to blame?

Oakwood School looked promising. Everyone welcomed me. Besides academia, their curriculum emphasised life skills and building resilience. But it seemed forever out of reach, a future intended for someone luckier than I. With a few words from Charlotte's mouth, everything had imploded. And everyone expected me to make heavy decisions. Ones that would decide the next years of my life. I still couldn't imagine leaving Portum and being without Lucas. Until now, everything had been status quo and Galactic Conquest. It wasn't conceivable that it could end or come close to ending.

The possibility of encountering another "Susan" remained likely. White Mountain School lay four years in the past at that point, but the memories still plagued me. I wrote a swear-filled rant on my experiences there, typing until I ran out of things to say.

Charlotte complimented me when she read it. 'It's good, Max. You're so descriptive and insightful.'

'Thanks.'

'Would it help if we burned it?'

'What?'

'We can burn it on the bonfire, at Citadel Woods. It might make you feel better.'

'It wouldn't.'

'That's completely understandable, I was only suggesting it.' She tilted her head, her eyes widening.

'Um, are you alright?'

'Yes. I'm just wondering if you'd like to try an English mock.'

'I haven't done any English since... never mind.'

'I think it's worth a try. Have you met Rosaline?'

'I've seen her.'

'I can ask her to work with you.'

'Are you sure?'

'You have a talent for the subject. She can see what stage you're at.'

'Ask her. I might try the mock.'

Rosaline taught English in the mainstream school. However, she had recently been transferred to Portum. Most of the students did their English work with her, but why would Charlotte "waste a resource" on me? I hadn't proven myself willing to learn. Surely, Rosaline would be better spent on someone else?

***

'Shouldn't the Capulets know about potions?' I challenged.

An amused smile danced across Rosaline's lips. 'Maybe Friar Lawrence just didn't tell them?'

'They've been fighting for years, right?'

'Yes.'

'And in all that time, neither family tried to use potions?'

'Why would they use potions?'

'Probably to poison or sabotage each other.'

'Max, I don't think Shakespeare was trying to write *Game of Thrones*.'

'No, he probably just intended to write a plot hole. Because that's what it's called Rosaline, a plot hole.'

Her giggle bounced across the room, creating ripples in the atmosphere. 'I really wouldn't write that in your exam.'

'Can the examiner not handle a different opinion?'

Days later, I joined my cohort for their end-of-year mock exams. I'd mostly purged *Romeo and Juliet* from my brain and hadn't touched anything else in the syllabus. Whatever impressive vocabulary I used, it wasn't enough to mask my lack of understanding. The exam demanded strict adherence to a mark scheme I didn't know.

It was a brave attempt, but I'd missed out on most of the curriculum. At this stage, attempting any GCSE would be difficult. Most students spend two years studying, and from year eleven I'd only have nine months.

***

«How did you do? » asked Bradford943.

«I screwed up on every question. So, I've probably failed.»

«To be fair, you never cared for it.»

«Nope, never did. And I still don't see why people love Shakespeare so much, *Romeo and Juliet* is utter shite.»

«See, there's your mistake, you question it too much. It's utter shite, but thinking like that makes it even worse.»

«How can you not think about it? It's in front of your eyes all the time.»

«I get on with it, like everyone else. Why can't you? I thought you didn't want special treatment.»

«True, I did say that. It's too late now though, nobody can do five exams in less than a year.»

«Well, not everyone. But you're good at pulling off impossible shit.»

«It's different on Galactic Conquest, I've got you guys. Besides, I can't abandon the Paladins to do stupid exams.»

«I don't see why you'd need to stop playing. We'll take over some of your responsibilities.»

«Like I did for you last year?»

«Yes, and once your exams are over, everything can go back to normal.»

«What about the Shadow Imperium? They're too much for one person to deal with alone.»

«To be honest, mate, I made a mistake last time. You're right, blocking them hasn't worked. Draxx just wants to bully us into merging.»

«We've talked about this before, its risky.»

«To get rid of them over the summer? It won't be easy but it will give you some peace of mind.»

«Hey, I'm good at impossible shit. Draxx might even listen for once.»

«He's never gonna listen. For your own sake, stop trying.»

«We built the Shadow Imperium together. I can't leave him to die with it.»

«Fair enough, but you're making a mistake in trying to save him. Anyway, if we manage to defeat them, you can do your GCSEs without worrying so much.»

Since December, the Paladins had fought a cold war with the Shadow Imperium. Draxx14 had asked me to merge multiple times since I had first refused. They would raid our Discord server and troll our members. Our plan to defeat them grew more elaborate by the hour. Bradford943 and IMaginkI would lead a team of carefully selected infiltrators.

Slowly they'd infiltrate the Shadow Imperium and sabotage it from within, thus paving the way for a full-scale invasion. Last time, we were unsuccessful in crossing the bridges to the fortress. This time, we hoped to take advantage of the chaos and rush straight for the capture point.

Utmost discretion was required to maintain secrecy. For this purpose, I chose the name Market Garden so any Shadow Imperium spies would think we were talking about the historical event—not a plan to cause their guild's destruction. Come July 4th, we were ready to initiate the operation.

Unfortunately, the annual Portum trip to Citadel Woods was on the same day. And without warning, dad forced me to go. I didn't have to stay overnight, but during the day I'd be stuck without internet access. Unable to monitor progress, all I could do was fear failure. If the Shadow Imperium discovered our intentions, it would mean war.

To say the least, water-gun fights and Super Smash Bros. weren't my cup of tea. So like every other year at Citadel Woods, I spent my time wallowing away on a bench. And counting trees gets boring after a while.

'What about exploring the woods?' Lucas suggested.
'Over the years we've done that fifteen times.'

'You actually keep count?'

'Nothing else for me to do in this shithole.'

'You're not the only one getting bored. I've convinced Christine to take us to the local playground. Wanna come?'

'Better than sitting here, I suppose. Any salt and vinegar crisps left?'

'I saved some for you, don't worry.'

'Thanks. I'll bring the water bottle from my bag. We can share it.'

Under the gaze of dusk, Portum students played on a rusty roundabout. I'd traded one withered bench for another, but at least Lucas was sitting with me.

'Want some water?' he asked.

'No thanks, I've had a lot already. You need some too.'

He took one sip and ended up gulping the rest. 'You're right, I'm super thirsty.'

'Well, it is ridiculously hot. Especially in this coat.'

'Why not take it off?'

'I don't know... It's not right without it.' A tired exhale escaped from my lungs. 'I've never liked it here, there's nothing for me to do.'

'I used to be like you, Max. Back home.'

'What do you mean?'

'I played a lot of video games, spent most of my time indoors'

'Did you lead a guild?'

'No, but I was in one. We used to fight against other players.'

'In my guild we fight people. Someone always wants to destroy us.'

Lucas glanced at the Portum students, all boisterously playing together. 'I know it seems like a big deal now. But one day you'll grow up, move out and get a job.'

'Is this about your internship?'

'Sort of. I've been worried about it.'

'You'd be great working there. And if they don't hire you, that's their loss.'

'Thank you, Max, let's hope you're right.'

Chapter 19: And Swings Again

19.7.17

Lucas, my dad talked to me about the possibility of your leaving this September. Apparently, you may really get the job you have always wanted. When he told me, I cried for a while, but not because I don't want you to leave. I'm only sad because our time together looks like it's drawing to a close.

Where do I even begin? Your art lessons inspire student upon student, and when you bring in your Nintendo Switch, it makes everybody so happy. You make me and others burst into laughter. Only now have I realised how much I've taken you for granted. You're one of the few TAs I connect with, and in our time together I have learnt amazing things.

No matter what, you have always supported me. For that, I'm eternally grateful. When I first came to Portum, it terrified me. On the first morning, Dad barely got me off the sofa. It took me years to feel comfortable. And to realise you're always looking out for me. So, whatever it is, I want you to know that I'll always care about you, no matter what.

Thank you, Lucas,

Max

On the last day of term, when Lucas received the letter, he read it out with me. By the time we finished, our eyes glistened with sentimental tears. We shared a fraternal hug, but a sense of finality loomed in the air. That inauspicious day saw the last hours spent at Portum for five TAs.

Jayden and I were close to them, we both bought them farewell presents. In a year, Portum had lost seven staff members; were Lucas to leave, it would be eight. Most of the older boys had left, and my cohort had taken their place. One age in Portum crawled to a slow end, but as always, a new one peered over the horizon.

If I'd wanted to stand a chance against GCSEs, I would have been wise to spend the summer studying. However, I lacked the discipline to do that. In previous years, I had begun the term attending lessons. But after a few weeks, I'd collapse under the pressure. In short, self-fulfilling prophecy blocked any consistent academic effort.

Then there was the possibility of Lucas leaving. We'd been a team for years, and I couldn't imagine Portum without him. Events on Galactic Conquest also weighed heavily on me. If our surprise attack on the Shadow Imperium failed, I'd be fighting a long brutal war, which would end any hope of GCSEs.

***

«They almost discovered us, mate. We can't keep this secret forever,» Bradford943 said. «School's already started in America, and it's about to start here.»

«The more we wait, the less of a chance we'll have,» IMaginkI added. «And the less time you'll have to prepare for GCSES. Nine months isn't long to catch up.»

«Hmm, I don't want a repeat of last year's defeat. As you know I'm on holiday in Brighton, and my dad's laptop isn't that great,» I fretted.

«Last year was a trap, this time it's on our terms. If we attack tomorrow afternoon, we'll have an excellent shot at it,» Bradford943 pressed.

«How close can you get our main force to the throne room?» I asked.

«We can open the gates and get them across the bridges. That's further than last time.»

It's a dice roll, I guess. «Then let's do it. I suppose I'd rather play with the odds we have now.»

Tuesday, August 29th, 2017, 7pm. My parents were out for a leisurely walk on Brighton beach. Our saboteurs sprang into action, assassinating enemy officers and opening the gates. We launched our attack at a moment's notice. There wasn't time for me to open Spotify. Adrenaline shredded our nerves as we charged across the bridges. *Draxx isn't here, good.* Ferocious corridor-to-corridor fighting consumed everything. The clashing of blades and the all-too-familiar sound of laser fire overwhelmed my senses. When Shadow Imperium reinforcements arrived, they slowly broke our cohesion.

Most troops were fighting in their own pockets around the fortress.

Encircled inside a barracks, and left with five minutes to take the capture point, misery and defeatism began to take hold in our ranks.

«When I throw the grenade, we'll make a run for the throne room,» I said.

One of my men faltered. «Sir there's only five of us here. The others won't reach us in time,».

«It's either that or we die here. Let's go.» From behind cover, I hurled the grenade at our assailants. The explosion mutilated their bodies, killing them before we could finish them off. Without another word, we darted through the corridors. My heart skipped a beat when we found the capture point undefended. *Of course, they're too spread out to leave anyone here.*

To win, we had to hold the capture point for three minutes. Bradford943 and IMaginkI's forces did their best to tie down Shadow Imperium troops. But the opposition we faced grew fiercer by the second. With five seconds to go, our lines collapsed under the strain. I closed my eyes, resigned to defeat. *It's war then. I still can't believe we almost won...*

«CONGRATULATIONS, YOUR GUILD, THE PALADINS, HAS WON THE DAY.»

«What the fuck?» I blurted. «How?»

The Shadow Imperium were evicted from their base. Everyone ran around like headless chickens. How on Earth did we do it?

«They probably didn't retake the capture point in time,» Bradford943 hypothesised. His was the widely accepted theory, because the Shadow Imperium only had five seconds left after defeating us. I bounced around our hotel room like a toddler on Christmas day, one who had eaten too many sweets.

**

«I've fought in your corner for years. And this is how you fucking repay me?» Draxx14 thundered. «Answer me you little shit. Be a man.»

My emotions were engulfed in a chilling coldness, the flame of happiness snuffed out and destroyed. «I did it because we felt threatened.»

«Bullshit. You and all the retards who follow you are traitors to the Shadow Imperium.»

«Don't talk about my friends like that. Can't we talk this out?»

«I don't talk to traitors. You and your dogs are dead to me.»

A melancholic tremor worked its way through body and soul. But I wouldn't allow emasculating tears to fall. «You're the fucking traitor,» I exploded. «How do you sleep at night, you fucking cunt?»

«I sleep very well, thank you. The Paladins and the destruction of what we built? That's your doing, never forget it.»

«Bullshit, all of us left for a reason, Draxx. All you ever did was whore us out to the Devil Dogs. You're a corrupt pig who sucks Diablous's dick all day.»

«I did what had to be done to ensure the Shadow Imperium's survival. Unlike you, I'm a true leader, looking out for everyone's best interests.»

«Best interests!? Nobody wanted to become a Devil Dog puppet except you. Fuck their purity and fuck your crap about being a true leader! Choke on your bullshit in your wet dreams, you rotten little cunt.»

«*Draxx14 is typing...*» Those words were enough to send my brain cells into a frenzy. Whatever his response, I stood ready to meet his fire with my own. No longer would I make concessions and excuses for him, his days of abusing me were over.

«You see, that's the difference between us. I'm a true leader and unlike you, I can control my emotions.»

In the atmosphere, an invisible darkness reigned. One born of long-held resentment and unbridled rage. «And a word of advice, the next time you insult someone do it properly. That was as pathetic as you.»

Draxx14 had become a bulldozer, crushing my ability to experience anything but anger, fear, and sadness.

233

Then he really got personal. «Or maybe the rumours are true. Paul? I always knew that was bullshit, what's your real name? Are you too cowardly to share it?».

«I'm not telling you anything, cunt.»

«You don't need to. I already know you go to a school for fucking retards. Face it, you're mentally ill, that's why you go there.» *How does he know about Portum?* «See that's the truth about you kiddo, you'll never amount to anything but a retard.»

Everything hurt, is this what they meant by heartbreak? «Now fuck off and go cry to your mummy about your ego. I got important shit to do,» he cursed.

I switched off the laptop, somehow suppressing the urge to cry.

***

«About what Draxx14 said yesterday,» Bradford943 began. «It isn't true. The Paladins surpassed 1500 members for a reason. There's nobody I'd follow but you.»

«Thanks,» I said.

«And we didn't win because of luck. You made most of the plan.»

«You're the one who helped execute it.»

«Yes, but you brought us together. Most of our empire is your hard work, be proud of it.»

«I am.»

«Good, because when I get back, we're going to discuss its bright future. Go enjoy Brighton, I'll see you soon.»

At that moment, IMaginkI sent me a message. «What if I told you we could hack Draxx14's account?»

«His Galactic Conquest account?»

«Yes.»

«Are you sure? We'll get arrested if the police find out.»

«Doubt it, they're too busy to investigate everything. And Draxx won't have any proof it was us. Besides, I've been working on a key logger and I need someone to test it on.»

«But he'll need to download it, right?»

«Yes, I'm going to trick him. But I'll need some information to do it, what's his real name again?»

«Darren Wilson.»

A few seconds passed. «I've already got his Facebook page, LinkedIn, Twitter, and a possible address.»

«Seriously? You're way faster at this than me.»

«Yep, here's a picture of him and his nan.»

Teeth gritted, I glared in disgust. They stood smiling, locked in a warm embrace.

«He's studying geology in university,» IMaginkI told me. «Girlfriend, job. Bastard has it all.»

I imagined Draxx14 screaming whilst being subjected to the cruellest tortures. *Gonna kill that fucker's family and make him watch.* I couldn't get the images out of my head. I hated him so much that I was certain I'd kill him if given the opportunity.

«You can get his password right?» I asked.

«Literally just contacted him. He has no idea what he's about to download.»

«Awesome, cunt deserves it. In the meantime, I'm gonna have some fun with the picture you sent me.»

In paint.net, I edited the image of him and his grandmother. I placed them in a rather compromising position. Our Discord server erupted in laughter at the sight.

'Draxx is a granny fucker!' I relished the insult.

Once IMaginkI had been successful, we waited for Draxx14 to go offline. That's when I logged in as him. *It worked! Time to die, motherfucker.* I took all his virtual in-game items, splitting it amongst those he tormented. *Wait, what if he uses the same password for his email?* He did, so I decided to send an email to his girlfriend and family.

I impersonated him, sending the indecently edited image I'd created and telling them that he enjoyed "child pornography on the dark web". My mouse hovered over the send button. *Go on, the fucker doesn't deserve the life he has.* With a mischievous grin, I pressed send. Finally, I'd achieved unlimited power, I wasn't weak anymore.

Susan, Draxx, everyone who I despised, they wouldn't stand a chance against me. I'd won. All my years of empire-building had paid off. For an hour or two, that's how it felt. But on Brighton pier later that morning, the sea air lacerated my empty soul. Once elation and adrenaline had faded, I found nothing to be proud of anymore.

***

For lunch, my parents took me to Eds Diner, my favourite restaurant. But as I threw up a facade of happiness, even the food proved tasteless.

'Darling, there's something we need to tell you,' mum lamented.

Gloom gripped my throat. 'What is it?'

Dad slid his phone across the table. 'It's better if you read it for yourself.'

31.08.17

Hello Nick and Lucy,

I hope you're having a good summer. I'm sure Max enjoyed Brighton and his birthday. I have news for you, I got the job at the place where I was doing an internship these last couple of months. It was so sudden, and everything was so rushed, I wasn't able to let everyone know straightaway.

I wanted to tell you last week, but the timing wasn't great because of Max's birthday. I believe that you, and more importantly Max, need to know before school starts. I don't want him disappointed on the first day. I am so sorry that everything was so rushed, and I am really grateful that you entrust-

ed me to work with such a clever student!

Thank you so much for everything, I will really miss working with your son. We've been through a lot, and he's become a big part of my career at Portum. Please show him this text, he needs to see it.

This isn't goodbye, I will definitely come to Portum one day and visit Max. Thank you so much for everything, Lucy and Nick. I wish you all the best. And I wish all the best for Max. He will have a great future.

Thank you,

Lucas

'Can we go back please?' I sniffled.

Maybe Draxx14 was right. I'd lost control of my emotions and subjected his family to emotional harm. His life had been destroyed, all because of our disagreement in a videogame. Did I truly deserve an empire? As they say, absolute power corrupts absolutely. Galactic Conquest wasn't the same anymore. That night I couldn't bear to look at it, let alone play. Combine that with Lucas leaving Portum, I'd sunk into the depths of depression. I didn't sleep much that night. I'd descended into the abyss, accompanied only by sadness and fear. Blinded by a need for power, I failed to see that Galactic Conquest wasn't about my ego or about beating people. I enjoyed playing because of the friends I'd made. When it became about defeating the Shadow Imperium, it failed to enchant me. In my arrogance, I had neglected my non-virtual self and hurt others. I stood up, guided by an almost supernatural desire to read Lucas's text again.

Each message held memories. Throughout all the time we'd spent together, he had stuck by me. *If you saw me now. What would you say? Crying.* Lucas's words rang repeatedly in my head. 'Come on, just five more questions. One last push, you can do it.'

Lucas was the first TA who believed in me, no matter what. Life seemed dire, on a collision course with total failure, and I hadn't always made the best decisions. But it wasn't too late to steer the ship and prove Lucas right. *I have to do it, for me, for you and for everyone.*

The decision faltered once or twice before I affirmed it. GCSEs in nine months wouldn't be an easy task, nor an instant remedy. However, for my future and to make Lucas proud, I was willing to give it a go.

***

«I support your decision,» Bradford943 said. «But you don't need to disband the Paladins.»

«I'm not ready to talk about why.»

«Fair enough. Good luck, XMA, and remember, you can always come to me for help.»

«Thank you, Bradford, for everything. I really enjoyed the Paladins while it lasted. It taught me so much and gave me more enjoyment than you can imagine.»

The online goodbyes were short. I had made a difficult, life-changing choice to alter my future. To succeed, I would need to utilise everything I had learnt over the last four years.

Chapter 20: Vindication

Inside my mind, I drew up the schematics of a plan, similar to the way I would on Galactic Conquest. To get into sixth form, I'd need to pass five GCSES in just nine months. With such limited time, spreading myself too thin was unaffordable. Thus, I chose to undertake three GCSES, all based on required workload and past success.

Mathematics and English Literature were abandoned from the get-go. Which left me with Religious Education, Media, and English Language. Three subjects instead of five eliminated much of the pressure. If possible, I'd spend most of my time out of the classroom. Stress had been a huge factor in the previous year's "breakdown", and I wasn't keen to let it seep in again.

A return to English class was already off the table. The single day Rosaline taught me English one-to-one proved more effective and more enjoyable than the entirety of my time spent avoiding pencils in that classroom. I'd do everything I could to ensure an easy transition year, because my plan was built on one cast-iron certainty: at the end of year eleven I was leaving Crown Heights for another school, whether that was Oakwood or somewhere else I found suitable. Beyond that, my next move in life's game of chess wasn't university. Rather, I wanted to take small steps in the right direction with the end goal of becoming an independent adult.

***

On the first day back at school, the bus had several empty seats, albeit one had been taken by a shuddering year seven.

I sat solitary, looking out the window and listening to music. This morning it was Slipknot, "The Devil In I". For me, the song's lyrics and shifting riffs reflected recent events online. *I went too far, targeting his grandma like that. No, think about what he did to everyone. You couldn't just let him carry on.*

'Max, are you coming?' Jayden asked. The bus had come to a halt, we had arrived at school.

'Oh, shit sorry.' I stuffed my iPod and headphones inside my bag. 'Coming.'

'Wait can you two help Simon find his way up?' the escort requested. She pointed to a tiny boy, frozen in the playground, unsure what to do.

'Yeah, sure.' I jumped off the bus, catching up to Jayden.

'How was your summer?' Images of Draxx14's parting words, and that night spent awake in the hotel room, washed over me.

'It was alright, I guess.'

'Hmm, OK.' We looked behind us, searching for Simon. 'Wait, where did he go?'

'There,' I pointed out. Simon pressed his palms together, utterly frozen.

'Simon, this way.' The rest of the journey was spent at a slower pace. The moment we arrived at Portum, Charlotte took Simon into the kitchen. *Just like she did with me in year seven.* Jayden went to catch up with the other boys, and I plotted my first move. *Lucas always checked the timetable. Good place to start.*

'And you know, Simon, we're all so happy to have you in Portum,' Charlotte chirped.

'Uh-huh,' murmured Simon. I entered the room, finding today's timetable on the kitchen counter.

'Sorry, just a moment please.' She strode toward me. 'Lucas isn't here, you know that, don't you.'

'Yes,' I replied, searching for my name on the timetable.

'Follow me. Sorry about all this, Simon.' *Why are you apologising for me?*

'Where are we going?'

'To your new room, I hope you appreciate it.'

Charlotte pointed to a door at the back of the computer room. If the chipped wooden frame was any indication, it was a poorly maintained oddity. When I opened the door, it answered with a weary whine. 'You're giving me the Turing Room? Didn't it belong to Carlos?'

'Yes, but he's not here anymore.'

'That's why I used past tense.' Cracked walls and peeling paint, the only table was a long slab of laminated wood. 'I need—'

'You can't have the Mondrian Room. And we can't be as flexible anymore. It's either this or you can be like everyone else. Do you know how many people want their own room? You're incredibly lucky to have one.'

'I know but—'

'Sorry, I need to get back to Simon. Tell me later.'

I shrugged, a heavy sigh escaping my mouth. *She'll come around. I'll just have to get a computer myself.*

I scoured the room for an Ethernet jack. Without access to the internet, my work would be a lot more difficult. Fortunately, one sat just under the empty noticeboard. A teaching assistant I was friendly with helped me find a computer and speakers.

***

'Hi Max, I'm here to do some English work with you,' greeted Rosaline. I spun around with eyes wider than the solar system. 'Are you OK?'

'Yeah, I'm fine.' *Good, that's gonna make things easier.* 'Can you give me a second to set this up?' She watched me hurriedly connect everything. But things soon came to a standstill when I realised I needed an extra socket for the speakers. 'Have you seen an extension lead anywhere?'

'I don't think so. Let me just bring in some chairs. We don't have anywhere to sit.'

'Right... I forgot about the chairs.'

'Yes, sitting down would be a start. Wouldn't it?'

I smirked. 'What's wrong with the floor?'

She began to chuckle. 'Nothing, would you prefer it?'

'No, I'm good with chairs.'

'I've got two here. And you needed something else right?'

'Yes, the speakers won't work without an extension lead.'

'I'll get you one later today, deal? I'd like to start English as soon as possible.'

'Hmm, alright, but I don't want to be without sound for too long.'

'OK, that's fine. Now, let's crack on with our English work.'

18.9.17

Dear Lucy and Nick,

This is just a quick note to let you know how brilliantly Max is working in his English lessons. I am teaching Max English every day and have been since the beginning of this term. He has impressed me so much with his focus and hard work in English. Every single lesson I have had with him he has worked so brilliantly, showing complete focus.

We have been looking at Heritage texts for the English language exam and he has shown a real understanding of text. Last week we were working on an exam question and he wrote an excellent answer. I would appreciate it if you could also give some praise to Max. I have been so impressed by his attitude.
Bye for now
Rosaline

For the most part, it was a breakneck blitz. I missed Lucas but formed great relationships with Caleb, Lily, and Olivia, the teaching assistants who worked with me. To avoid the crowd's in-between transitions, I arrived early and left five minutes before the lesson ended. It didn't help develop my resilience, but I wanted an easy last year.

***

Charlotte shuffled her feet, arms crossed. 'I hope this isn't the start of you regressing.'

'I prefer to do the classwork in Portum.'

'That's fine, but we still expect you to attend classes.' *She'll come around eventually.*

***

The approach I took to learning was rarely orthodox. Instead of slaving away at homework, I inspected the resources intended for teachers. My guiding motto was: "understand how it works or hit your head against the wall" – nobody could bring themselves to disagree.

Ironically, the exam techniques I developed were methodological. I'd have exact sentence starters and an exact number of paragraphs.

To prevent myself from feeling overwhelmed, I retained only the important information. I'd also seen progress in other areas. At my grandmother's 80th birthday, I gave a speech in front of a crowd. Through sheer endurance, I learnt to tolerate water on my face in the shower.

Online, I'd become community manager for a project recreating a closed children's MMO (massively multiplayer online game), which without getting too technical was a manageable responsibility. One day when we completed our work, I hoped to share my involvement on a shiny CV. As ever accompanied by music, I discovered my favourite Disturbed song, called "Rise".

On Galactic Conquest, music sponsored every battle. At my first mock exam, it was a galvanising war cry. A week later, Charlotte and Rosaline bounced into the Turing Room, beaming ear to ear. Jayden and I exchanged a bug-eyed glance.

'You got an A on your English mock!' Charlotte exulted.

'That translates to a seven,' Rosaline added. 'Seriously well done, you should be proud of yourself.'

Jayden gasped, 'You got a 7? Holy shit!' He pumped his fist in the air.

'Jayden, language,' Charlotte scolded. 'Just to re-mind you.'

He groaned, hand slumped on the desk. One mock exam defeated, two to go and then the term would be over. Because of my successes, Rosaline convinced me to take English Literature as a fourth GCSE. The next mock wasn't until February but we began studying anyway.

***

My gaze fixated on a shed, barely large enough to hide in. Mum and dad stood behind me. In front, a head-teacher twirled around.

'Any questions, Max?' she asked.

'Oh, uh.'

'Go on, you can ask. Are you interested in our gar-den shed?'

'How many students do you have here?'

'36. You'd make 37.'

'Right...'

I left the small complex with bowed shoulders, searching for a bench. Dad sat with me, passing a bottle of water. 'It's fine if you don't want to go there,' he said.

'It's too small and too far from home. I'd probably end up hiding inside the shed.'

Mum pressed her lips tightly. 'It has a mainstream like Portum.'

'That's my point. I already struggle, so why move from one Portum to another?'

'Right, I don't know what we're going to do then. That just leaves us with Oakwood.'

'I'll visit it and then weigh up my options. I don't want to choose until I've seen them all, even if it ends up being the lesser of two evils.'

'We'll probably be at tribunal if you choose Oakwood.'

'I didn't get this far without you fighting.'

***

Disaster struck before my final mock exam. Our central heating broke, and a migraine poisoned me with a crushing pain. Nonetheless, I revised and though drained, still wanted to undertake the exam.

Lily tried to console me. 'You're gonna smash it, you know that, don't you?'

'Hopefully.'

'Most of our kids wouldn't be able to catch up like you have. You're brilliant, don't forget it.'

I nodded weakly, 'Thanks, just doing my best.'

'You need to give yourself more credit. Down there I babysit SEN, up here I help you do something great.'

I nodded weakly. 'Thanks... I'm just doing my best.'

A tiny smile escaped my mouth, but it grew into a huge grin when I entered Costa Coffee. 'Lucas, you still come here?'

He smirked. 'Ha, you've found my little secret. How are you doing, Max?'

'About to do an RE exam. I had no idea you still come here.'

'Well, what can I say, you've converted me.'

Emboldened by a chance encounter, I charged the exam head on. Days later, at the end of term. Arthur and Lucas surprised us with a visit, Jayden and I bolted towards them the second they entered Portum. A thrilling end to the term indeed. On New Year's Eve, I sat in bed basking in my achievements.

Presumably, I had passed all my mocks, Charlotte's faith had been restored, everyone was proud. And I'd continued to work as a community manager, forging new friendships and working towards a common goal online. For once, things were going well.

***

'It says here I got a nine in RE!' I said exultantly. 'Are they serious?'

'Yes, seriously. Well done, Max,' congratulated Rosaline.

Charlotte sauntered over, admiring the paper with my mock results. 'You know, you could stay for sixth form.'

Four months ago, you wanted to throw me out. Guess the numbers are all that matter. 'How would that even work? You told my parents I couldn't stay.'

'If you pass four GCSEs, and we believe you will, then you'll be able to do level two courses in sixth form.'

'Don't people go to sixth form for A-Levels?'

'Not always,' said Rosaline. 'But I'm friendly with the English department. If you do well enough on your exams, I'm sure we can bend the rules a little.'

Very few students get a nine. In old money, it translates to an A Star or, more specifically, between 80 and 100 percent. In just three months, I'd achieved every teacher's dream. For Portum, it's a shining example of success, affecting the outlook people now have on the provision available there. Charlotte wanted people doing well in sixth form, so bending the rules and shifting her limited resources to me was a no-brainer. Shortly after receiving my results, I made an application to Crown Heights sixth form. However, this was a safety net, not a firm choice. Did I really want to stay at Portum, or was five years a good place to end on?

Charlotte had remained rigid, always telling my family that come July 2018, I would have to leave Portum. Those words sent us into a spiral of uncertainty, and for months, we feared I'd be condemned to a vegetative state at home. Now that she had shifted the goalposts, I couldn't help feeling somewhat miffed.

Lucas, Arthur, and several other TAs had left, my cohort and I were growing older. Sooner or later, Portum would welcome a new generation. I cared for a lot of people there but had also come to a crossroads in my life. The era of secondary school and Galactic Conquest was wearing thin; the choices I made now would determine what would take its place.

Come March, I'd made two visits to the Oakwood sixth form site. I saw an opportunity there for a new start. It was a much more mature environment than Portum, and being a private school gave them more flexibility. In crossing the bridge to adulthood, I would need more than academia.

The school was alien to me, but they placed emphasis on what I needed, life skills. I'd have three years to mature and catch up with my peers. It would be a leap and a half, but perhaps I needed that push to grow. I still loved Portum and had little time to choose between both.

After three years of delay, the local authority was close to finalising my EHCP. I had until the end of March to decide on a placement. With mere weeks to make such a life-changing decision, I looked to my closest friends and former TAs for help.

11.3.18

Lucas, it's been a while since we last spoke. I hope you get this message; I'm sending it on my dad's old iPhone. Oakwood school has offered me a place, and I need to decide before the end of the month. Like you I've become attached to Portum, and it's difficult for me to think about leaving it behind.

The opportunities at Oakwood completely eclipse what Portum can offer with its limited resources. You always said I have difficulty moving out of my comfort zone. Guess you're right. If I go to Oakwood, I'll face that difficulty head on. Things are changing, and I miss you. Just the other day Jayden and I were talking about the time we all spent together.

What is your advice, Lucas? How do I choose the right path?

Best wishes

Max

11.3.18

Hi Max,

I'm so pleased to hear from you. I understand what you're going through, and it's a tough decision to make, especially for your age. Unfortunately, I can't give you fair advice. There are so many variables, like what you want to do and which sixth form can help you achieve it.

It's scary to think of the unknown, so learn about it. If you research your options, it won't be as scary. And you'll make a better-informed decision. Now, if you think Oakwood completely eclipses Portum then I think you should go for it.

It's easy for me to say, "Do this, do that," but in reality, it's a million times more difficult. In life we always face change and challenges. It's like a videogame, you start in a fun green-grass area and get comfortable. Then you move to another location. It is nice in the grass area but it's not helping you level up anymore.

You need to level up to progress in the game. That means eventually facing the final boss. Do you remember when you told me about your first day at Portum? You said it was so scary. But you met a lot of awesome people, and I think life is always like that. We cannot escape change, but it isn't an enemy. It helps us level up and make new memories.

Oakwood will be completely different to Portum. However, I'm sure they have some awesome things there. Don't get intimidated, it's not gonna be like prison, there's a lot of fun stuff waiting for you there. I mean, look at you now. If you think about it, all you do in Portum is revise and take the test. Most people would think that's hell.

But it's not like that at all, is it? There are awesome things in between the challenges. And if it turns out Portum is the best option, that's great too. You'll continue to be challenged there; A-Levels aren't easy. Change will always be here, Max, no matter what you do. But it isn't an enemy. It helps us grow and expand our world.

Always feel free to message me when you feel pressured. And don't forget that you've got a lot of people to support you. It's not you vs the world, Max. We're all in this together.

Lucas

It took me almost two weeks to decide. But after consulting everyone, listening to their advice and weighing everything up, I chose Oakwood school. It wasn't an easy plunge, but in the long run it would be a fresh start, providing me with valuable time to mature. Portum had prepared me for the next step, and not taking it would be a disservice to all they had done for me.

Chapter 21: Descent

On my knees in a fuzzy Portum. Draxx14 towered above, his muscles forged from steel.

'You thought I wouldn't find you?' he challenged, striking me in the face. 'A little kid versus a grown man. Who do you think wins, Max?' Steel pressed against my lips, the barrel of a gun. 'Get the fuck up!'

'Holy shit,' Jayden called.

'Draxx, don't kill him,' I begged.

He pointed his gun at Jayden. 'My name is Darren.' A muzzle flash followed by a horrible bang.

'No!' I screamed.

Morning dawned in my grandparents flat. A terrible crippling void pursued my every movement.

'Are you checking your emails?' grandma asked.

'I'll be off before Baba gets out of bed. Don't worry.'

'I'm sure he won't mind. You have a lot of work to do. When's your first exam?'

'May 14th. Don't worry I haven't been studying all night.'

'I'll give you a few minutes, don't worry.'

The dream flashed in my mind, what did it mean?

And why did I have it? A search for answers brought me to my old Discord account, the one I used for Galactic Conquest.

«I'm sorry you still feel this way about it,» IMaginkI said. «I thought we'd only steal his Discord account. Didn't think you'd do the rest.»

«I just re-read the last conversation I had with Draxx. I'm never going to do it again, it's too painful.»

«You can cut him from your message history.»

«That won't stop me finding it again. So I'm deleting both my old Discord and my Skype account.»

«You don't have to do that. But if it's how you feel, I won't try and dissuade you.»

'Max, are you coming?' grandma called.

'Another two minutes please, I'm deleting something.'

«Before you go,» IMaginkI began. «Congratulations on the mock results. Have you considered a career in IT yet?»

«IT?»

«You asked me to teach you a few things, remember? It's a diverse field, I'm sure you'd find something.»

«Thanks, I'll consider it. Hopefully we'll speak again one day.»

I didn't think deleting my accounts would bring me peace. I'd still brought harm to Draxx14's family, nothing could change that. However, with GCSES on the horizon I found myself desperate to get over the haunting memories.

Now I was left with two Discord accounts. I used one for my duties as community manager and the other to communicate with Jayden outside of school. *Don't tell anyone about Draxx, they won't get it.*

***

'We'll have to tell the parents about Citadel Woods,' Charlotte faltered.

'Might have to cancel it,' Christine said.

I was hidden behind a wall, eavesdropping. Citadel Woods wasn't my favourite trip by any means. But I recognised and respected its importance to the other students. Dad told me that at the last social evening Charlotte begrudgingly accepted donations from parents. I'd also heard other worrying things about Portum, though it didn't need rumours to see the signs. Mr Haddaway, Charlotte's manager, took three months to replace a chair, valuable TAs had left, and fundraisers were seldom permitted. I was concerned for the future of the unit, so, fearing that I'd only get evasive answers from the staff, I launched my own investigation, hoping to find out if Portum was in financial trouble or at risk in any other way.

After watching where Rosaline placed her fingers on the keyboard and making a few educated guesses, I found out her password, which gave me access to her staff email and the school's network drive, which contained all sorts of information, such as annual reviews, incident reports, and other passwords for various things. They were all stored without protection, so anyone with network drive permissions could open them. I spent a few days combing the network drive, transferring the "important" files to my private cloud storage. Eventually the "useful information" ran out, and to obtain more I decided to try accessing Christine's emails. As the co-head of Portum, she'd be the likely person to handle what I was looking for.

Most Portum staff stayed signed in, their computers left unattended. It wasn't hard to get inside the office and start transferring Christine's emails. Why her in particular? For personal reasons Charlotte hadn't been coming in as often. So Christine was my only choice.

You're doing this for Jayden and the others. Might make up for Draxx's family and prove him wrong about you. Footsteps, belonging to Christine. Easily recognisable and edging closer. *Shit, it's not done transferring.* Caught in the adrenaline, I bolted to the Turing Room. *I forgot the USB!*

Inch by inch, the Turing Room door crept open. 'Can I come in?' Christine asked. 'I think I've found something that belongs to you; it says it's copying something.'

She blocked the exit, her illegible stare stuck in permanent equilibrium. 'Shall we take a look?'

'I-I don't think I've been in the office today.'

'I'm sure you haven't. Which is why I'm wondering how it got there, and how you know about it.' Begrudgingly

I followed her back to the office. She pointed to a file on the screen. 'Could you delete that? It says email, I think that's what it copied.'

I cut and pasted it into another folder on my flash drive. 'It's gone.'

'Can you make sure?'

'Pretty sure it's deleted. Gotta go to RE now, bye.' I ran out of the office, not daring to look back for a second. *Got the USB, close call.*

'Lily's already here, and I'm sure she's fine with waiting. Can we have another look?'

'Oh, uh, I lost my USB when I ran.' The USB stick was in my pocket. But she didn't know that, at least I hoped not.

'We'll find it between the three of us. Don't worry.'

A parasitic sickness ravaged my stomach. The search took over an hour, I didn't tell them I'd hidden it in a pencil pot. When they couldn't find it, in came the "big guns", two smartly dressed men, both assistant heads. They arrived in a desolate Portum, with few staff and no students but me.

I recognised one of the men, Mr. Haddaway. His conspicuous ears and vexed shoulders always gave him away. He stopped to raise an eyebrow at some student art-work, before trudging into the kitchen. As Christine updated them on the situation, the room turned into a sauna from my point of view.

'Can we search your coat and bag?'

'Do I have a choice.'

'You have a choice to be honest. Wouldn't you like to leave?'

Might delay them, besides there's nobody around. I removed my coat. 'Nothing inside there, knock yourselves out.'

The assistant heads watched her pad me down. When she didn't find anything in the coat's pockets, she rummaged through my bag.

'Go to the Turing Room, Your dad will be here soon.' I grabbed my bag, exchanging a callous stare with Mr. Haddaway.

I searched through the pot of pins and broken rubbers, only to find the USB stick missing. *They must have found it, so why aren't they letting me go? Must want to teach me a lesson.*

Dad arrived, escorted into the room by Christine. 'I'll leave you both alone,' she said.

'Bit hot in here,' dad remarked.

'You get used to it.'

He took a seat, crossing his arms. 'You need to tell them where it is.'

'They've already found it.'

'I know. Unfortunately, they want a confession.'

'I haven't committed a crime. I'm just worried about Portum, that's why I did it.'

'We don't have time for this, we're going to be late for Naomi.'

'Fine, I'll confess or whatever. Let's go.'

Around the table sat Christine and her two superiors.

'It's in my room, pencil pot,' I admitted.

'Thank you, that's very mature,' Christine said.

I made eye contact with Mr. Haddaway, repressing a boastful smirk. 'Got other confessions too.' His eyes narrowed. 'I bypassed your web filter with a proxy server. And I figured out Rosaline's password.'

'Thank you for telling us, Max,' he said. 'Mr. Baker and I will speak to your father now.'

I was left with Christine, who shadowed me wherever I went. She followed me into the garden, sitting with me on Alfie's memorial swing.

'Do you mind if I join you?' she asked.

'You already have.'l

'I also had trouble with honesty as a child.'

'Yes, you've said that before.'

'You have an impressive memory.'

Hands in pockets, regret trickled down my spine. 'Sorry it was copying your emails.'

'Apology accepted. But that doesn't explain why you did it. Or why you needed Rosaline's password.'

I pointed at the kitchen.

'Did you do it because the kitchen's too noisy?'

'No, I'm fine with eating in there.'

'So why did you point to it?'

'Because it won't always be there, are we making it count?'

'What do you mean?'

'I'm talking about Portum. Is it financially safe?'

'I can't answer that, sweetheart. But it's not your concern, in a month you'll have done your GCSES. And I think you'll be at another school.'

'Maybe you're right... When will I get my USB stick back?'

'Tomorrow.'

'If it's not in my hands by then, I'll get it myself.'

They scolded dad and told him that Portum wasn't experiencing any difficulties. But for me, that wasn't a good-enough answer. I got back to work as soon as I arrived in school the next day. Ready to break into the network again.

'Awfully hot in here, isn't it?' Charlotte remarked. 'You must be boiling in that coat.'

I spun around, switching off my monitor. She and Christine had entered the room.

'Five years, you get used to it.'

'Were you not expecting us?' Christine asked.

I leaned back. 'No. Is this about yesterday?'

Charlotte sat across from me. 'You're so much better at technology than I am. But we want you to know that

Portum is safe, and that you're safe in Portum.' *You always say that.*

'Last year we lost seven teaching assistants. That includes Lucas and Arthur.'

'We miss them terribly,' Charlotte said. 'And you know we're doing everything we can to replace them.'

'You're replacing them with agency staff who aren't permanent.'

'Caleb's one of them, he's amazing, isn't he?'

'I really like Caleb, but for all we know he's gone next term. It's hard to get experienced staff when we keep losing them.'

Christine bit her lip. 'Worst-case scenario, we might have to move schools—'

'Don't worry about it, that's our job,' Charlotte interjected. 'You know, we've always found you so caring and insightful. So I'm telling you this because you'll understand.' She took a deep breath. 'About Portum... we have had to block some things.'

'Like what?'

'We can't tell you,' Christine said. 'Just know that we're doing our best. Don't worry about us, focus on your exams. We want you to do well.'

'But you can't look through our emails again. Or do anything dangerous with the school computers.'

'Fine, I won't do it again.'

'Good. Please, please don't do it again.'

Christine had suggested Portum moving schools in a "worst-case scenario". And as for Charlotte? What exactly did she "block"? I believed something very was wrong, and I wanted to get to the bottom of it.

'One USB stick,' Rosaline said, handing me the device.

'Only took them three days to delete something. Even my mum can do it faster.' The sliding mechanism was broken. 'Great, now I need to open it with a paperclip. Bastards.'

'Language, Max.'

'Do you know how annoying that is? I have to remove the entire chassis without damaging the memory.'

'Well, I'm sorry to hear that, but you shouldn't have tried hacking the school computers. You've got your exams soon, none of this is necessary.'

'OK, I won't do it again.'

'I've got to pick up my son. I'll see you tomorrow,' she paused, hand hovering over the door handle. 'Seriously, Max, please don't do anything like that again. You have a month left, that's it.'

With Rosaline and Lily at my side, I had nothing to fear from exams. I'd practised with them for months and had developed a systematic approach to answering each question. A return of self-belief and confidence inspired me to remove my hood. On the day of the first exam, I took it off and never wore it outside again, (except for when it rained, of course). I was given an exam laptop to type my answers, and extra time alleviated any remaining pressure, albeit I'd often finish without making use of it. In between exams, I searched for and found a new way to break into the school's network drive. Without getting technical, there was an exam account for students using a laptop to type their answers. They'd forgotten to block access from said account, so upon entering the username and password I could just walk right in.

***

'Hey, Max,' Caleb said in greeting. 'I'm here to take you to get your lunch on the high street.'

'Oh, uh, give me a moment.' I minimised the network drive, invisible heat swamping my face.

'What are you up to?'

'Nothing, just listening to music. I paused because you came in.'

'Have you listened to System Of A Down yet?'

'No, been busy with exams.'

'Can I put it on?'

'Sure, if you want.'

I watched carefully, hoping he wouldn't see the network drive open.

'This is a good one. It's called "Chop Suey".'

My foot tapped rhythmically. 'Strong drummer. Can't believe I didn't listen to them sooner.'

'I'm glad you like it.' We spent the next few minutes sharing music. Memories of doing the same with Arthur and Lucas flashed throughout. In Caleb, I saw bits of both former TAs.

He studies it, you can trust him. 'Wanna see something cool?' I opened the network drive.

'How did you get in? Social engineering?'

'Let's just say they left a few backdoors open.'

His eyes widened at my explanation. 'That is seriously clever.'

'Mostly luck, but I've picked up a few other tricks over the years.'

'Have you seen Jayden anywhere?' Sophie asked. 'Sorry, did I startle you both?'

'No, um, we haven't seen him,' Caleb replied.

She peered at our screen. 'Is that the network drive, Caleb? I thought you didn't have an account yet.'

'Uh, it's another drive. Computer magic, you wouldn't get it,' I sputtered.

'I don't know what you're doing. But be careful, you've really scared Christine.'

'Right.'

'Caleb, I think you're taking Josh to maths. If Max hasn't had lunch yet, Christine will handle it.'

'Sorry, forgot about lunch,' I said.

'Nah, don't worry about it, I had fun here.'

***

Just as I sat down for a late lunch, the fire alarm boomed. Jordan covered his ears, falling into a flood of tears.

'Damn it, not again,' I chided.

'We still have to go downstairs,' Christine said.

'I know, but I'm taking my food anyway.'

'I'll carry the cutlery for you.'

We survived the barrage of students, suffering hard collisions along the way. Somehow, neither of us dropped anything.

Draxx14's words rang in my mind: *That's the truth about you, kiddo, you'll never amount to anything but a retard.*

'Max, are you alright?' Christine asked. 'We're here now.'

'Yes, I know where we are.'

I planted myself on the grass, an agonising rift opening in my chest. It wasn't hunger, food didn't vanquish it. Jordan wiped the tears from his eyes, comforted by several TAs and Portum students.

'See, this is why we need someone at the fire alarms.'

'It's a good idea, but we don't have the staff for that,' Christine said.

'Just have them at the main ones for ten minutes or so before an exam.' I pointed to Jordan. 'You can prevent that and disruption.'

'You'd be good on the student council. I'm sure we could find a way to make your ideas work.'

'Think I've had my fill of leadership, thank you. Besides, I'm happy just being a community manager. It's less responsibility.'

'I don't know what a community manager is, but it sounds important.'

'It is.'

'By having your fill of leadership. Do you mean you were on the council in primary school?'

'No, but I was the supreme leader of the Paladins.'

She met my gaze with a slack expression. 'Right, OK.'

'We had 1500 people, I led them all...' My eyes watered, any source of light gleamed and left behind trails. 'I had this rival... Draxx14, in real life his name's Darren.'

'Is this online?'

'Yes. You know what I did to him?'

'No.'

'I hacked that bastard's email. Then I-I told his filthy fucking family that he was a paedophile. Ruined his life.'

Her eyes grew wide with both shock and confusion.

'Yeah he, uh, he wasn't really a paedophile. But I sent his address to paedophiles on the dark web. He got raped.' The last part wasn't true, I haven't ever been on the dark web, let alone in contact with paedophile rings. But it didn't matter, I wanted her to see my "power".

I sighed heavily. 'Forget it, look at me now. I'm eating my lunch on the grass.' Just metres away from us, mainstream pupils engaged in teenage bravado. They either gossiped loudly or pushed each other for no apparent reason.

'And you want me to be on the student council?' I scoffed. 'Like those idiots would ever vote for a Portum student. You know how they see us.'

'No, I don't.'

'Let me enlighten you then. The truth is they think we're retards, and that we'll never be anything else.'

'Why do you think that? Did any of them say—'

'They rarely say it, but always they think it.'

'OK... if that's how you feel.'

I'd repeated Draxx14's words, but I didn't know if I believed them. Was he right about me? Was I mentally ill and unable to control myself? Why did he appear in my dreams? And for that matter, why did I tell Christine? She didn't understand, and perhaps nobody would ever understand.

Chapter 22: Fallen into Defeat

I'd finished four GCSEs and done everyone proud. Come August, I would be back in school collecting my results. A good ending if the local authority agreed to fund a placement at Oakwood. They still hadn't sent us the final EHCP document, so we were still waiting on their decision.

But for now, after months of hard work, I could finally relax, though it wouldn't hurt to see everyone on the last week of term.

'Mum, I'd like to go in next month. Just to say goodbye.' Her gaze met the floor. 'Is everything OK?'

'The school thinks you're on the dark web.'

'What?'

She cleared her throat. 'They think you're in touch with a paedophile ring on the dark web.'

'Why would they think that?' I scoffed. 'I've never touched it.'

'Be careful with what you say. Some people take it literally.' *Christine! Damn it, I wasn't thinking straight when I said that.* 'Apparently you're hacking their computers, too, but that's beyond me.'

Sophie or Caleb. One of them must have written a report. 'Dad and I have been called in for a meeting with safeguarding. Don't tell him I told you though, he's under a lot of pressure already.'

'OK.'

I approached Dad the moment he came home. 'Can I go to school tomorrow? I want to see everyone.'

'I'll text Charlotte.' He took out his phone, hovering a finger over the screen. 'There's no ulterior motive is there?'

'No,' I lied.

The last time safeguarding had been involved was when Susan accused my parents of allowing me to access pornography online, which could have had disastrous consequences for my family. So I wasn't willing to take any chances. I needed to know if I was in danger, and that required me to question people.

***

Sophie scratched her nose. 'Never wrote a report about you.'

I motioned Jayden outside. He waved away any potential onlookers. 'Are you telling the truth?'

She responded with a hesitant nod. *You wrote a report tell the truth. Why do people bother lying to me?*

'The last time this happened, my dad nearly went to prison. Can you see why I'm concerned?'

'I think you're worrying too much. I never wrote a report about you.'

Fine, you'll have to live with the guilt then. 'You're not dishonest, so I'll give you the benefit of the doubt. You're free to go.'

She hurried out, not daring to give me another glance.

'How did it go?' Jayden asked.

'She's definitely going to tell Charlotte. But that's OK, it gives me a chance to clear things up.'

'Shall I do anything else?'

'No, you've done enough. Thank you.'

'Alright, I'll see you on the bus.'

Seconds after he left, Charlotte rushed into the Turing Room. Her chest puffed out, eyes fixated on me. 'Sophie is terribly upset. She said you questioned her.'

'This is all a huge misunderstanding. Do you have questions, I can clear everything up. I've never touched a paedophile ring, I'm telling you.'

She moved a chair close to me and sat down. 'I don't have a question. But there have been reports to say—'

'That I'm some child sex predator?'

'No, and nobody has said that. The reports say you've been on the dark web and are in touch with a paedophile ring.'

Fuck, why did I have to lie? Draxx was right about me.

'You told two people that you gave the email address of someone who'd beaten you on a game to paedophiles on the dark web.' *That's not even true, I only told*

273

Christine. And Draxx didn't beat me. The Shadow Imperium lost. Fuck it, I'll just have to explain everything simplistically.

'And I think you emailed, as if from him to his family. That's nothing to do with paedophiles.'

'May I?'

'Yes.'

'I used to play a game online, in which I led a guild. We called ourselves the Paladins, we had over 1500 members.' The memories flooded back, from all those times Draxx14 tried to destroy the Paladins. To my triumphs and all the moments I enjoyed on there.

'That game was the Wild West. And my biggest rival, Draxx14, in real life his name is Darren.'

I paused as the world seemed to shrink before my eyes. 'Sorry, where was I?'

'You were talking about a boy called Darren.'

'Right, Darren. He and his followers did everything they could to destroy us. I-I got angry and lost control; my ego got in the way. In the heat of the moment, I proved him right.'

'Proved him right?'

'Never mind. All you need to know is I got into his email and destroyed his relationships. The rest isn't true, I just said that crap about paedophiles to feel powerful.'

A harrowing silence loomed over us. Charlotte clutched her chin. 'I, uh, sorry. I'm amazed at how very skilled you are. And I'm so relieved to hear you telling the truth.'

'What about the reports?'

'Out of our duty of care, and also out of our love and concern for you, Max, we needed to write those reports. I had no choice but to send them on, because it's school policy. However, you've made a very clear statement there. And I will share it with the safeguarding team.'

Once she had left, I did a puzzle with Caleb. He answered what he could, telling me that Christine ordered him and Sophie to write a report. The situation had mostly been cleared up, but I'd need to come in for a meeting with Mr. Haddaway and Mrs. Walton, the school's safeguarding lead. Coincidentally, it was on the same day dad and I had an appointment at my feeding clinic.

***

'If you hadn't hacked our network or whatever,' Rosaline said. 'You wouldn't have to deal with this silly meeting.'

'It's too late now. Why is Mrs. Walton wasting her time with me, anyway? There's probably kids doing heroin downstairs.'

I assure you, nobody is doing heroin downstairs,' she chuckled.

'You know what I mean. There are lots of kids who need her, and she's wasting time on me.'

'Well, she's got serious things to handle. But your safety is a concern to her.'

'Except I'm perfectly safe, and she's the twat putting me in danger.'

'Language. You've done great on your exams, don't let this ruin it. Finish the meeting, and after that promise me you won't do any more hacking.'

'I promise.'

'Seriously, no more hacking. There are a lot of things I'd do for you, but wrestling with the FBI isn't one of them.'

'Come on, you're my partner in crime. You can't just abandon me,' I joked.

'Maybe Jayden will do it for you. Speaking of which, I need to teach him English. Good luck.'

Inside one of Portum's small rooms, Dad, Mr. Haddaway, and Mrs. Walton sat around a table.

'Welcome, we've all been talking about you. Have a seat,' Mrs. Walton said in greeted. *Guess this is the naughty corner.*

'Max, do you have a computer at home?' she asked.

Did you just bring me here to ask that? 'I've had one since I was eight. If I've done well on my exams, I'm going to build one for my birthday.'

They both shot thundering glares at dad. 'Yes, if he's done well, I'll buy him the parts,' he said.

'Do you use the internet, Max?' Mrs. Walton asked.

'Yes, since I was three years old—'

'Who might want to cause you harm on the internet?'

'I'm not finished. Do you know what exactly I do on the internet?'

She crossed her arms. 'I'd like to find out.'

'Previously I was a powerful guild leader. Now I'm a community manager, responsible for the safety of over 10,000 users and counting. Some of those users are children.'

'So you're aware of E-safety then?'

'I have to be or our game project will be shut down.'

'I see, thank you for telling me.'

'What you're investigating happened three years ago. If you're interested, pop up to Portum another time. It's a long story. Now if you don't mind, my father and I have an appointment to attend.'

She eyed a ghostlike Mr. Haddaway.

'We're just going to have a little chat with your dad,' Mr. Haddaway said. 'You're free to leave now.' Ten minutes later, we were driving away in the car.

'What did they say to you?' I asked.

'They called me irresponsible, but thanks to what you said we're OK.'

'I still don't understand how those idiots got their jobs. We never see Mr. Haddaway in Portum, it's insane how he's the manager.'

'They seemed a little off. I lent Mrs. Walton one of my books about teenagers, but she didn't say thank you.'

'You shouldn't have done that. She'll never give it back, let alone read it.'

'Don't rock the boat. They've been good to you.'

Dad never saw his book again. I'd gained some valuable information about Portum, but in doing so, all I'd accomplished was the destruction of trust. The Citadel Woods trip went ahead, albeit the students weren't allowed to stay overnight because of new safeguarding policies. I didn't go that year, but seeing Jayden and others loudly complain made me feel sorry for them. Perhaps I was right to worry about Portum's future, even if it "wasn't my place". I came into Portum on Tuesdays and Thursdays, strictly barred from all computers. Mr. Haddaway forced Portum staff to shadow me at all times.

Charlotte encouraged Caleb and me to find a computing course for me. She wanted to "put my skills to more constructive use". I found CompTIA, and took their IT Fundamentals certification, to test the waters. Caleb paid for our study guide; we'd be studying for and taking the exam together.

That and going to Costa Coffee, kept me coming in. Months before, I'd grown slightly tired of Portum, and now the whole place seemed withered. I bought presents for my TAs using my own money, hoping for a pleasant farewell. In September, I'd hopefully start a new life.

***

'Max,' mum lamented. 'The council has finished your EHCP.'

'Did they say no?'

'It's ridiculous, they ignored all our reports.'

'Even Naomi's? She's known me for years.'

'They've ignored everything, no OT, no extra support. You're staying at Portum.'

The EHCP was disgusting, unfinished sections, most people's input cut out, cries for help ignored. 'We're getting a solicitor,' I declared. 'This is bullshit.'

'Solicitors are expensive. Dad won't—'

'Dad never gave up, and neither will I. It took them three years to write this utter garbage, and I'm not putting up with their crap any longer.'

'It might be better paying for someone to help you at Portum.'

'Portum is dead. It died last year when everyone left, it's an empty shell now.'

'But what about Rosaline and—'

'I'm done with it. It's time to move on. Staying there is living a lie and delaying the inevitable. We're getting a solicitor, and dad will agree.'

'If that's what you want. I'll always support you. But going to tribunal isn't easy, I've read about it.'

'It's never been easy, and it's never going to be easy.'

Re-mortgaged and money borrowed, we were mobilising for all-out war with the local authority.

***

'You've got a lot of hospital appointments this month,' Rosaline remarked.

My throat crooked and curvy, eye contact impossible. Those "hospital appointments" were meetings with various solicitors. I hated lying, but the coming tribunal war was a sensitive subject. My parents and I had agreed on one of the most experienced firms in SEN law. To get into Oakwood, my EHCP would need to change. That meant proving I needed a high level of support, and that would require professional assessments and well-fought law-fare. And I'd have to stay at Portum for an unknown period.

'It's so fab you're staying,' Rosaline beamed.

'Yep.'

'What did you think of history class?'

'Teacher was nice, I guess.'

'You'll be even better at A-Level English.'

I shrugged. 'I'll just take history, the EPQ thing and that computer course, whatever it is.'

'Are you sure? I think English will be better, we can do it in Portum.'

'It will be enough UCAS points, won't it?'

'Yes, I suppose it will. You don't meet the requirements for level three courses, but I'll convince them to bend the rules for you.'

When my parents told Charlotte about the tribunal, she confronted me the second I came into Portum, dumping sheets of paper on my desk.

'It's the Portum curriculum,' she said. 'We can offer you a lot.' A year ago she said they could offer nothing but academia, so what had changed? 'You're staying with us for the time being. You know that, don't you?'

'Yes.'

She started reading, but I didn't want to say anything, lest I offend her. 'We don't have the resources they have at Oakwood. But we can help you learn some life skills.'

'Such as?'

'...to recognise some items as potentially dangerous,' she read. 'Scissors, sharp knives, and hot equipment. I think you've learnt how dangerous those things are.'

Are you trying to guilt-trip me? Charlotte had lost me at "playing only age-appropriate games." Time was fleeting, I needed a drastically different approach to learning. Portum had faded, its time was over for me. I had contemplated my decision to leave thousands of times. It hadn't been easy to make. We were already going to face off in court, and I didn't want the fighting to reach Portum. People I cared about would get caught in the crossfire. Charlotte wouldn't tell the local authority that Portum couldn't meet my needs. So I believed she was taking this personally.

In a last-ditch effort to explain my decision, I wrote a letter. And left it on her desk.

18.7.2018

Dear Charlotte,

I know you want what's best for me. I'll always be grateful for that, and for everything Portum has provided for me over the years. Unfortunately, as the saying goes, all good things must end. I have chosen to pursue a one-sided tribunal case against the local authority.

This is to secure my place in the Oakwood Sixth Form centre. You care about me, and you don't want me to be disappointed if I don't win. I understand wanting to protect me and to keep me safe. But I'm not the tiny muffin-devouring boy in the bright-red uniform you met all those years ago. In my years at Portum, I've experienced a lot. Anger, sadness, disappointment, fear, pride, love and joy. You're right, I will be upset if I don't win, but I have learnt that life isn't positive all the time. Bad things will always happen, and I must face my own demons. Nobody can teach me that, it's something I can only learn through experience. That's why change isn't an enemy, it teaches us.

You always compliment me and flamboyantly talk about how "insightful" I am. But I'm still just a child, with a lot to learn. I only started going outside without wearing a hood two months ago. And a little over year ago I told you to "Get on your knees." I claimed not to remember, but I do. At the time it was easier to lie, because I wouldn't have to admit responsibility and face the consequences. Year ten was a difficult time for me.

I hated the boring work; I hated the crowded staircases and hallways. A lack of confidence and mounting pressures caused me to break down. Anger took over my rational mind, and I felt powerless to say anything. Yet I was also guilty, to the point of purposefully hurting myself, an act that I immediately regretted.

During that time, I ignored the good things and didn't ask for help. I confided in my large, rapidly growing empire. Over there, I was powerful and confident in myself. I gave over a thousand people something to believe in, and defeated those who wanted to destroy us.

Life outside the game proved too difficult for me to handle. But eventually I realised that hiding from it was both unrealistic and unsustainable. Eventually, I lost passion for my empire, and things I loved started leaving me. People I loved started leaving me, everything collapsed right in front of my eyes. And I'd been too wrapped up in my ego to see the bigger picture.

Only when Lucas, the last pillar, fell to the floor did I see it. Lucas, Arthur, my place at Portum – all gone. It seemed hopeless, but when faced with an opportunity to prove myself, I took it. GCSEs are the first non-digital commitment I've ever made, and doing them in nine months is something I'm immensely proud of.

The magic of Portum is gone for me, I don't care for A-levels. And whilst I'll always treasure it, it's time for me to move on. I don't want to be sheltered here forever. Life awaits me and I'll experience times both harsh and great. And about Portum. These children might not realise it yet, but they need you.

From year seven we come here with one guarantee. We'll change, and you won't be able to shelter us forever. There isn't much patience in today's education system, you're facing hard times. But I ask you to remember Alfie Robinson, the man who created Portum. He's proud of us for persevering, even if he isn't here to say it.

I'll always appreciate Portum, and I'm sorry the story has to end with a tribunal. At Portum you teach us to do our best, even if it seems impossible. Alfie wanted that too. And it's what I'm doing.

Thank you, Charlotte, for everything,

Max Toper

Charlotte called the letter "beautiful and insightful". It reduced her to tears. Mission accomplished then? Well, no, as Charlotte still refused to acknowledge that Portum couldn't meet my needs. Any hopes for a quick end to the conflict were shattered. But I'd laid the foundation for making amends after the coming war.

***

To combat the fracture in my heart, I confided in the internet. It was a quiet night, spent in my bedroom with the curtains drawn, participating in a podcast, which was one of my duties as community manager. Full of giggles, technological lingo and conversations I never saw myself sharing in real life.

The Discord notification bell rang. It rang again, five times more! My throat tightened. *What... I didn't say that.* Eager chatter defeated by eerie silence. Falsified screenshots of me vilifying community members posted in our private chat group.

«Max, you're being exposed,» Leonidas jested, his tone a chilling spear.

Betrayal. I ripped off my headset, squeezing it tightly. *Why would Barry and Leonidas do that?* Hours devoid of comfort. This sort of thing was supposed to remain in Galactic Conquest. Yet it had followed me here. Leonidas hadn't said a thing, and Barry had banned me from his server. I pleaded with Cole, the leader of our project, but he said nothing.

«Leonidas, please be honest with me. Where did you get those screenshots?» I demanded.

«I don't trust you with this dramatic flair you're adding to your messages right now.»

«Of course I'm being dramatic. Someone is trying to frame me. None of those messages look like my writing.»

«Cut the shit, Max. Sounds straight from a badly written sitcom with just-as-bad actors.»

Several minutes, no response. I initiated a voice call, flesh crawling with fright. He picked up but didn't say a word.

'Listen, if this was me, you'd have worked it out months ago. You're clever.'

'Mm-hmm,' he mumbled.

For three torturous minutes, I stammered. Until he chuckled ominously and left the call. Quarter-past midnight, a haven destroyed in a few gruelling hours.

I lay atop the bedcovers; heat moulded the duvet into my clothes. Sunrise gleamed through gaps in the curtains. *Have I even slept?* The alarm read 4:32. *Leonidas! Fuck, I've lost it all...* Groggily, tiptoeing out of bed, I checked Twitter. Cole had replaced me with my predecessor.

After all my contributions to his project, I'd been practically erased from existence. *Don't just jump in. It never worked on Galactic Conquest.* It took a lot of discipline, but I prevented myself from engaging with it for that day. I decided it was best to let things settle, then tackle them the next day.

***

Play my cards right and it might be over quickly.

'Max are you alright?' Oliver asked.

'I'm fine.'

286

'I got your drink, is this the right one?'

'Yep, that's an iced chocolate. Thanks.'

It coursed down my throat, and for a moment, I was free. Then I remembered last night's betrayal, and the void of pain ravaged me once more.

**

The last day of school passed slowly. Jayden perched himself in a corner, his TA Sophie having left for university. Would I see Caleb again? Without him, I'd have to study for my CompTIA certification alone.

Charlotte wasn't there, and Christine was buried in paperwork. As for Rosaline, she worried I wouldn't win the tribunal. On the bus ride home, I listened to "Firefly" by Breaking Benjamin. I knew, that when I returned to Portum that September, I'd would be the only year twelve. Zach, Jordan, and Adrian had all left. The Portum of old had vanished.

**

I waited for Dad to leave the house, then logged onto Discord. *Please, please don't let it be public.* My reputation didn't appear ruined, but being removed from Cole's server must have caused commotion, as it was the largest in our community. Rufus had sent me three messages. He was one of our most skilled programmers. Despite being only a year older than me, he claimed to know «more about software engineering than anyone who has a master's degree». *Could turn my computer into a paperweight if he wants.* Rufus wasn't someone famed for kindness. He spent much of his time insulting our followers completely at random, even people he hadn't interacted with before.

Cole prevented me from intervening. «It's not our platform. So we can't be responsible for his behaviour.»

I clicked Rufus's profile, bracing for impact.

«How could you do such a thing?» he challenged me. «I mean, I wasn't mentioned but, like, why though, what's the point?»

I'm screwed. It was either reason with him, or don't and be in a worse position.

«Please, listen, those messages are not real. We both know it's easy to forge them.»

«Listen to me, jackass. If you want a chance of being forgiven, you're gonna give us as much info as possible.»

Just like the old days with Draxx. «Can we voice-chat? it will be easier to communicate.»

He started a call. 'I already forgive you, man.'

'I don't want you to forgive me for something I didn't say.'

'Yeah, because everyone loves you.'

'What do you mean loves me?'

'God your accent is just... Can you stop talking, please?'

I did as he asked but started recording our conversation. What he said about everyone "loving me" and how he downplayed it was slightly suspicious. If it turned out he was the one who framed me I could use the recording to prove he told untruths.

'It's obvious you said it,' he insisted. 'And going offline for a day doesn't help your case.'

'I went offline because—'

'Not finished talking, shut up. Did you say this shit or not? Last chance to tell the truth.'

'I would never say anything like that.'

'If I find out you're lying, I will fuck you up, OK? Like you're lucky you're not banned from everywhere right now.'

'Are you giving me a chance to prove it wasn't me?'

'Yeah, sure, whatever. I don't have time for your shit.' He ended the call.

**

Anyone can forge a text message, but who did it? Another matter entirely. *Why do I keep fucking up?* Breathless wind. My solitary tears a whisper in darkness. I didn't resist the urge; crying a necessity. Attempts at sleep were met with a universe of dread. A relentless pounding plagued me, but I fumbled to my feet. Naïve efforts to protect Portum? They ended in failure. Draxx14, I sought only to earn his respect. Why couldn't I see he hated me? Why did I go so far to hurt him? From birth, a traitorous body had seen me mocked, vilified, or hunted. Now, circumstances had brought us to a debt-creating tribunal. And somewhere in this selfish world, a parasite had cruelly stolen one of my few treasures online. *Every fuck-up, every betrayal my fault.* Susan, Draxx14, the local authority and now an unknown enemy. *Does the world like shitting on me?*

Tortured memories swirled, each one a blade. 'I'm not a good person, wasn't born perfect. I guess nobody is,' I blurted. 'Heh, talking to myself, must be insane. Tonight is July 24th. Four years ago I led the Light Paladins' revolution.' *Did that my way. Did GCSEs my way.*

'To the person who has framed me, whoever you are I will find you. And to the local authority, I didn't come this far just to surrender now.'

My gaze met two boxes, a keyboard and a mouse. Once set up, I could configure them to glow any colour I wanted. These objects were bought three months ago, for the computer I was going to build. I'd arrived in the shop with grandpa and grandma, who had watched as I purchased it with my money. Afterward, I treated them to lunch.

Maybe it's time to ask for a birthday present.

Chapter 23: Summer Of Woe

You might wonder what the hell just happened, I certainly did. One minute life seemed to be going well. The next I was fighting a tribunal against my local authority and was experiencing yet another betrayal online. So who are Cole, Rufus, Leonidas. and Barry?

Let's start with Cole, leader of a project to revive an online videogame.

(Just to clarify, this game he's trying to revive isn't Galactic Conquest.) When you play an online game – like Galactic Conquest, for example – you're connecting to a computer called a server. This book isn't about software engineering, but simply put, without said servers being online you cannot play the game. Servers are expensive to maintain, and if the service (in this case a videogame) isn't generating enough profit, the servers are closed down and thus the game is no longer available.

Cole and his fellow software developers, Rufus and Leonidas, were trying to reverse-engineer the software the servers ran before they were closed. If they succeeded and could host their own version of said servers, then everyone could play the game again. However, the videogame wasn't his intellectual property, so the company who originally owned the game could stop him at any time. This, and the fact he was trying to revive a children's game, means there are certain rules he must follow to stay in their good graces.

Cole was a university student in Canada in his early twenties, trying to lead us in a revival effort. Leonidas, who had recently graduated from university, was also in his early twenties and lived in the United States. Rufus was a year older than me, also lived in the US and was a software developer on the project. There were more developers on our team, but my story isn't about them. What you need to know is that these three are masters of their craft. If you own an electronic device with a computer in it, and you get on their bad side, it's done for.

Our project had followers, and I served as their community manager. My job was to coordinate our moderation team, manage our social media, and serve as their mouthpiece. In Rufus's words, «When you speak, a little part of us speaks.» And before I can end this exposition dump, there is one other person, Barry, who I need to cover. Barry wasn't a member of Cole's project, but was a prominent member in our online community. Certain people perceived he had an ego, and thus he was overtly disliked. Despite this, I befriended him and agreed to always help on his podcast. It was this voluntary effort, dedication and activity that earned me

Cole's respect. After my predecessor left, he chose me to be community manager.

Somehow, Barry and Leonidas came into the possession of messages, horrible messages that someone had edited to make it look like I'd sent them. They showed Cole, and he removed me on the spot, no questions asked.

Fortunately, my reputation hadn't been destroyed. They had swept everything under the rug, and Barry had edited the part where I got confronted out of his podcast. I presumed that whoever had framed me believed that I'd fade into obscurity. However, some people inside the project were still loyal to me. Most of them hadn't believed the fake messages. And though I'd been banned from Cole's Discord server, I could still communicate with my followers. But this didn't mean the enemy had given me an advantage on purpose. For all I knew, someone wanted to hold my reputation hostage with blackmail. The battle lines had been drawn.

On one front, the local authority was determined to deprive me of the help I so desperately needed. On the other, an unknown enemy hunted me in the shadows. A bitter war had broken out, and its outcome would decide whether the future was to be bright or harrowing. I had two objectives, victory at the tribunal and proving my innocence online. Coordination with solicitors, courts, and educational professionals is difficult. And with its heavy caseload, I could assume the local authority would take longer to mobilise. Events often unfolded faster online, and thus I focused on that theatre for the summer.

And a summer of woe it was. My parents were already under pressure, so I didn't dare tell them about the second front. Speaking of which, I used probing tactics on the battlefield. With a resurgence in my activity, I believed the fox would be flushed from his den, unable to resist finishing the job.

***

«Expect an official statement regarding my resignation soon,» I said.

After leaving me to linger for a day, Cole finally replied. «Sure, but I'll run it by the rest of the team.» Four agonizing days crawled by. *All the things I did for him, and he can't give me five minutes.*

«Cole I'm sorry but this is upsetting me. If I get nothing back in a day, I'm posting the resignation message I sent you.»

Time elapsed, still no response. On our community forum, as a legal requirement, all posts had to be approved by a human moderator. So I needed a sympathetic staff member to help. Fortunately, I used to oversee the moderation team. One of them, Sebastian, agreed to help me.

«I've let it slip past,» he said. «Are you sure they won't take it down?»

«They won't, it would cause too much uproar,» I replied.

«Well, it's receiving a positive response, mostly.»

«Ah, so we've drawn someone out then.»

«You have, but I bet you won't want to see who.»

«Why not?»

«It's Barry and Leonidas, they're saying shit behind your back.»

«In Cole's Discord server?»

«Yep. Here, I'll send a screenshot.»

I read the messages, heart plummeting lower with each one.

«Max got demoted. He didn't resign,' Barry spilled.

«I have to say it is suspicious,» a community member remarked.

«We've been trying to keep the drama a secret. We don't want to disturb the community.»

«What drama?»

«Let's just say he was working against us all.»

«How is that even possible?»

«We're not saying anything else. Stop asking,» Leonidas scolded.

«Hey, if you guys want to be quiet. Why are you talking about it in our community's biggest Discord server?» Sebastian interjected. That's where their conversation ended. No more messages.

«Bastards,» I cursed.

«If I had to guess, they're the ones who framed you,» Sebastian hypothesised.

«I have considered that. But nobody's guilty until I have firm evidence.»

«Fair enough, but I got an idea that might help.»

«Go on.»

«You know Discord tokens, right?»

«Rufus asked for mine once, don't know why he wanted to access my account.»

«Yeah, Rufus has gotten away with sketchy shit before. Basically, I'm going to steal Barry's token.»

«I get what you're saying. We break into his account and find out how he got the fake messages.»

«Yep, never liked him anyway.»

It's not like Draxx, I hope. «He'll never consent to giving you his token. So how will you get it?»

«Give me a few weeks. Trust me, I got this.»

If there were other avenues for proving my innocence, they weren't visible; I had to take Sebastian's word for it. But that didn't mean I placed all my eggs in one basket. If Cole would let me back into his Discord server, the perpetrator wouldn't be able to resist another attack. I made a heartfelt appeal to my former colleagues, hoping to pull on their heartstrings. If successful, Cole would unban me. In the event, only Rufus responded.

«I forgive you, my friend,» he said.

«There's nothing to forgive me for. I did nothing wrong.»

«Bruh, stop lying. I'm not against you, but if you wanna get anywhere, you need to stop lying to me.»

The room moved at lightspeed, yet I was stuck in slow motion. «I'm not lying to you. I'm sick of this, I just want things to return to normal.»

«Bro everything is normal. Tbh, everyone forgot about you.» *Barry was talking crap behind my back just days ago.*

«And you're not returning, lol, that's for sure,» he continued.

«I can't fix this then.»

«So leave. Trust me, you not being here will make us feel a whole lot better.»

«I just feel this rush of cold upset coming over me. Please, is there anything you can do?»

«Yo, imagine how we felt when we saw those messages.»

«I never said those things. Why on Earth would I want to sabotage your project? I worked hard on it, but in another way.»

«Fuck off with the dramatic crap. Appeal denied, dude. Stop trying to push it.»

«Can't you talk to Cole for me? It's hard not to be broken, I have to fight a tribunal that's gonna put my family in debt for years. And I've lost everything on here.»

«What do you mean tribunal?»

Fuck, how do I explain this to him. «Well, I was born with autism, dyspraxia, etc.»

«Yeah, so was I, lmao. Listen, this is where you stop talking. I tried to reach out and say goodbye, but you're trying to make me feel bad for you, and I don't appreciate the manipulation.»

«Rufus I'm not trying to manipulate you. Please give me a chance to explain everything.»

«How is it not manipulation? This is gonna sound rude, but we're gonna formally respond to you later. OK? Thanks, bye.»

Four weeks into the second front, and nothing had been achieved. Every push ended in stalemate. With August in its last weeks, I had to face the reality that this theatre of the war I was fighting would drag on indefinitely. Sleep became a chore, laying down on the covers, bogged down by heat and melancholy.

I was probably the only fifteen-year-old (yes, it was still not quite my birthday) in the country not thinking about their GCSE results. Charlotte and Rosaline came back into school especially to see me open the envelope.

'An eight in English Literature,' I announced. 'Seven in English Language, another seven in RE. And a C in media studies.'

Rosaline's pupils bounced up and down. Everyone was beaming except me. Their excitement soon departed, as a big-boned awkwardness made itself known: the tribunal. Nobody wanted to say anything but it loomed over us like the proverbial elephant in the room.

***

Everyone congratulated me on my GCSE results. Yet despite it all, it was impossible to summon up much happiness. The war pursued us to Brighton; not wanting to ruin our holiday, I resisted using Discord for as long as possible. But that only shielded us from one theatre of the conflict. To prove Portum that couldn't meet my needs, we needed expert reports. And the psychiatrist we instructed to write one lived in Brighton; the appointment had to go ahead.

'He can't swallow a tablet,' said dad. 'Early on he was isolated from other children.'

'He's always in his own world,' mum remarked. 'Only stopped eating dinner in his bedroom four weeks ago.'

'Don't want to ruin my new computer,' I chuckled.

'You're very fond of computing. Are most of your friends online?' asked the psychiatrist.

'I had few friends before the internet.'

'What's stopping you from making friends in school?'

'Portum is like a fallout bunker, all the corridors outside are super narrow. You got hordes of teenagers coming at you from everywhere. That's why most kids don't enjoy going into the mainstream.'

'You used to wear a coat and hood everywhere, too,' dad added.

I stood up, collecting my coat and putting it on, face concealed under the hood.

'Until three months ago this was me. Not only at school, but everywhere outside the house.'

'Why?'

'Don't know, wasn't inspired by Kenny McCormick or whatever. Either way, I've taken it off permanently now, unless it rains.'

'You took it off starting with your first GCSE exam,' dad pointed out. 'Come to think of it, you never told us why you did your GCSEs.'

'Lucas left, I wanted to prove him right and everyone else wrong. Don't care for A-Levels though. My time at Portum is already finished, I need to go my own way.'

'What do you mean by that?' inquired the psychiatrist.

'Well, like I said, I don't care for A-Levels. I've outgrown Portum. It's been good to me, but it's over. I can see its flaws, I need somewhere that will help me become an adult, and Portum just doesn't have the resources to do it.'

'What about while you're still there?'

'Bide my time and stall my A-Levels until I can leave. It's not the best plan, and I don't want to upset anyone, especially Rosaline. But I have no choice.'

I tried to distract myself with studying for my CompTIA certification. But soon I could not resist the urge to fight again.

***

«Seb, I came online to find this.» Attached to my message was a screenshot. Barry's alternate account. The profile picture was that of a young girl.

«Yeah, that's his alt, but why is it important?» Sebastian asked.

«If you paste her image into Google, it brings you to her mum's Facebook page. They're friends of Barry's family.»

«Are you're saying he's a paedo?»

«Who knows? I'm just wondering how Kaylee's parents will think about him using their daughter's face as a profile picture.»

«I see where you're going. We'll make him look like a paedo and ruin his rep.»

«Only if he's the one who framed me.»

«I'm fairly sure he is. Anyway, I finished the malware. It steals Discord tokens, I made an alt and sent it to Barry. I'm waiting for him to open it.»

It's a pattern, same place, same hotel. I'm about to do something I'll probably regret.

«Dude, are you there?» Sebastian prompted.

«Sorry, I was getting a drink. That's impressive, how does it work?»

«Thanks. It's literally just a file with a trojan in it.»

«So, he clicks the exe, and it runs a DLL injection that grabs his token?»

«Yeah, you're learning fast. He'll only see a useless program.»

«If he launches it, that is.»

«Say he does, and it is him. What will we do? You've already said you don't want to fuck up his account.»

«No, I've done something like that before and I'd rather not do it again.»

«Fair enough. Hopefully, he'll open it soon.»

«I'll give you a hand, I'm good at manipulating people.»

«What should I say?»

«Tell him you're living in Brazil, in a house with six people. And that it would mean the world to you if he could test your software.»

«Right, I've made my English worse and everything. But what if he doesn't buy it?»

«Then we'll appeal to his greed or something. For now, let's play the waiting game.»

Two intense hours later, it's 11.30pm and Barry has only just responded.

«He says he'll open it in a bit,» Sebastian informed me. «He says he eats a "LOT at dinner". But he is a fucking land whale, so that doesn't surprise me.»

I giggled under my breath, trying not to wake my parents. «Have you done any more research on him?»

«Yeah, check this out, man, I found a picture of him on his school website.» Barry wearing a tight-lipped frown, his head bowed, face partially covered by an over-grown fringe. A thin T-shirt made his splotchy belly all too apparent.

«Truly a land whale,» I smirked.

«Yeah, I think it's a boys and girls' club or something. Can't believe they let him in.»

«It's not, I'm on the page you got the picture.»

«What the hell is it then?»

«It's a provision for autistic kids.»

«So he's retarded?»

«Possibly. But it's weird acting against someone in a provision like me.»

«What do you mean? He goes to school like us, it doesn't change jack shit.»

«You're right, forget it. Let's hope this works.»

«I'm so hyped right now, man, he's such a faggot.»

«Same, it'll be nice to get some answers.»

«Say we get proof that you're innocent. Will you leave the community if they don't take you back?»

«Tbh, I don't know. I've made a lot of friends here, but if this is how they're gonna treat me, I'm not sure it's worth staying.»

«Yeah, see Cole keeps people based on replicability. In my opinion though, he never deserved you.»

«Thanks man. I hope this works.»

«Wait, he opened it.»

'Fuck yes,' I whispered, barely containing a shriek of joy.

«Wait, failed, didn't send the needed DLLs. Hold on.'

Eyes shut, legs trembling. *Come on, I want the truth. Please.*

«I HAVE HIS TOKEN, MISSION ACCOMPLISHED!»

I was so pumped that I bounced up and down. «Fuck, yes!»

Sebastian felt the same. «Dude, my adrenaline levels are through the roof right now. I'm actually in his account,» he burst out.

«You're a fucking genius, man.»

We took a minute or two to catch our breath. Finally, I was a step closer to answers and to my first victory of the war.

«I'm in. Lemme share my screen with you,» Sebastian said.

«Right, I'm recording the whole thing. Open that group chat with Rufus and Leonidas. What we're after might be in there.»

Finally, the truth. A tremor in the heart. It fractured, smashing into pieces against my ribcage.

«I'm sorry, didn't think it would be all of them.»

Rufus, Leonidas, Barry, the three of them had orchestrated it all. From the forged messages to discussing slandering me in public. Rufus had vilified me the most, mocking all my heartfelt messages. Though he was unaware of my ethnicity, he called me a racial slur too obscene to publish. They knew where I lived. Leonidas had joked about all three of them meeting in New York. From there, they'd fly to London and show up at my house.

«He'll shit himself, lol,» Leonidas cackled.

«I still haven't got his old job, are you both working on that?» Barry asked.

«Community manager? Cole doesn't want to risk any more replacements or whatever. Sorry,» Rufus said.

«I thought you could convince him to make me CM.»

«We promised nothing. Besides, didn't you have fun doing this?»

«I guess so, he didn't deserve his position. I spent three years here, and he just comes along and gets everything.»

«Yeah, it was bullshit, man,» Leonidas said. «But he'll be gone soon, don't worry.»

All available oxygen screamed out of my lungs. Time fled from existence, bones froze over and begged to escape the prison of the skin. I suppose this begs a lot of questions. Since they were willing to show up in real life and harass my family, why not call the police? Or report them to Discord? Why not show Cole and thus prove my innocence? In the meantime, how were Sebastian and I supposed to explain how we got this information? Everyone would ask questions, and hacking is a crime. It was also very unlikely that they'd try flying from the US to London. It was expensive, and they wouldn't risk their livelihoods just to upset me.

Though shaken, I moved quickly, ensuring all my parents' accounts were private and that they were unreachable to my newly unmasked enemies. A woeful summer was over, but the war had truly begun.

Chapter 24 – At Arms

«How did you know that alt was me?» Barry asked.

«You told me ages ago. I just caught you using it today,» I replied.

«True, #exposed. I've been trying to have two personalities, hoping people won't notice.»

«I've never judged you on some of your stranger behaviours. But impersonating a twelve-year-old girl? No offence, but that's kind of creepy»

«It's for fun, kind of like a roleplay thing. Don't worry I've met her IRL. She was thirteen in that picture, and turning fourteen soon.»

«That doesn't make it OK. Ask consent before dragging her picture around Discord.»

«When you put it that way it sounds creepy and bad. I just keep random pictures of people I meet.»

«You're using a picture of an underaged girl as a profile. Is Kaylee her actual name? Are you impersonating her?»

«Yes, but it doesn't matter. Nobody has to see it.»

That was all the evidence I needed.

***

«Alright, Seb, I got him to admit it.»

«This might backfire and kill our rep, are you sure we can't destroy his account?»

«I'll never want to destroy someone's account. Have you found anything on his Facebook page?»

«Yep, there's people making fun of his autism and stuff. They're from his school.»

«Perfect, let's work on the video.»

My newly built computer, a fully operational battle station. A purple glow emitted from the keyboard and mouse. "Lights Out" by Breaking Benjamin roared at full volume as I put together a defaming video. Meanwhile Sebastian stoked up agitators online. An hour later, almost everyone saw Barry as a creepy stalker and potential predator.

«Dude you're a genius,» Sebastian complimented me. «Look on Facebook, someone's threatening to beat him up at school tomorrow.»

«All I did was bring people's hatred for him to the surface. Couldn't have pulled it off without you though,» I said.

Barry would go on to suffer months of bullying and what he described as "panic attacks". It was both my first major victory in the war and a devastating revenge. Most importantly, it sent a message to Rufus and Leonidas: I wasn't going away. They didn't know Sebastian had hacked Barry's account and discovered their plan to depose me.

But I hoped putting pressure on them would provoke a heat-of-the-moment confession. Provided I did nothing to undermine Cole, they wouldn't be able to frame me for trying to destroy his project. If that didn't work, the backup plan was to make a video leaking the group chat they'd had with Barry, thus proving my innocence and earning them everyone's ire.

***

17.9.18
Lucy and Nick,
it's wonderful to see how Max is taking the additional demands of sixth form in his stride. Maybe he will change his mind and stay with us.
Charlotte

School hadn't been easy. From the moment I dragged my sleepless body out of bed, a parasite attached itself to me. For the entire day, it festered inside me, consuming every emotion but melancholy. With all my energy conscripted to supporting the war effort on both fronts, I'd be tired and grumpy in the mornings, unintentionally holding up the bus and angering our escort.

Upon first reading that email, I saw Charlotte's agenda as belligerence. Awkwardness and fear stalked our conversations together. Because she was an opposing witness, I had to choose my words carefully, as any information she learnt could compromise my case. I didn't enjoy secrecy, but I felt it necessary to protect myself and those I cared about. Unfortunately, complete shielding proved impossible. In a SEN tribunal, it's imperative to buy in professional witnesses. Usually, they'll visit the school to assess the child or young person and write a report. Bluntly put, the local authority had their experts, and we had ours. However, for Rosaline and other school staff this meant being observed, filling in forms, and answering questions. I hated everyone being caught in the middle, but it was unavoidable. As for my lessons, if I was going to leave soon, what was the point in doing them?

To appease everyone I continued attending, resilience waning with every lesson. The only academic thing I cared about was studying my CompTIA certification with Caleb. We did it ourselves and enjoyed learning the material together. If I had any energy in between the battles, studying for the exam was the one thing I would do.

At any moment, my online enemies or the Local Authority could strike a crippling blow. Anxiety loomed and depression had taken an ugly hold. Amidst the internet warfare, dreams about Draxx14 returned to haunt me on a never-ending loop at night. Dreams in which we'd either hurt or forgive each other. I wanted to make amends with him, but believed it would never happen. Our friendship all those years ago had long since fractured. Video games, being with people who cared about me, and listening to music all kept me going. Lyrics became more relatable than ever, and I attributed particular songs to the different battles I faced. "Lonely Day" by System of a Down described the horrible parasite that drained me every day. And Disturbed's new songs seemed more appropriate than ever. "A Reason to Fight" literally inspired me to keep fighting. "Watch You Burn" reminded me I wasn't alone in being betrayed. And "Uninvited Guest" held my feelings toward Draxx14 in its lyrics.

***

«What part of permanently banned do you not understand?» Rufus challenged. Out of the blue, he and Leonidas had invited me to a private group chat.

«This is a lovely surprise, haven't spoken to you two since August. How you doing?» I asked.

«Answer the question,» Leonidas demanded.

«I'm permanently banned, I understand that.»

«You're lucky to even be in our presence after what you said,» Rufus jested.

«Seriously, why haven't you left the community yet? Just curious, sorry if this comes off as rude.»

Cunts. «No offence taken; I haven't left because I still enjoy it here.»

«Yeah, yeah, whatever. We're here to cut you a deal,» Leonidas chastised. «We saw what you did to Barry. He got physically assaulted because of your bullshit.»

Amidst the sweat, my lips mustered an involuntary smirk. «I'm sorry to hear that.»

«Oh, fuck off!» Rufus fumed. «Deal is simple, fuck off or we'll fuck you up. This is your only warning.»

«Watch your back, asshole,» Leonidas warned. They quit the group chat, leaving me enveloped by a furnace of fear. They had taken off the sparring gloves. Now, in addition to snide remarks on all social media, suspicious links and programs were sent to me from "anonymous" sources. They had failed to intimidate me into silence, and so resorted to other means of destroying me. I foiled their plans whenever possible but didn't know the full extent of their skillset. So I needed to advance the frontline before they made their move.

On a night when my parents were out, I approached Cole. If I could get unbanned from his server, I'd be a step closer to proving they framed me.

***

«Cole, I'd like to thank you for having me as your community manager. Although it didn't work out in the end, I learnt a lot from the experience. And it's one of my proudest accomplishments. However, what happened has really upset me, and I can no longer ignore it.

312

I stand by my claim. Those messages aren't real, someone has forged them and successfully framed me. But instead of your team investigating, two of your developers, Rufus and Leonidas, have harassed me. It's heart-breaking because you all inspired me to study for an IT certification.

You haven't responded to any of my messages. And without communication, I believe there won't be a resolution here. As you're online at the time I'm sending this, I ask that you open a dialogue with me over voice-chat. I'm dealing with a lot in real life, so it would mean the world to me if you did this.

Thank you,

Max»

Gripped by anxiety's grasp, I waited. Minutes later, Cole initiated a voice call. I took a deep breath and entered the maelstrom.

'I've been reading all your messages,' he said listlessly. 'I just haven't responded. Do you have proof they've harassed you?'

'I can invite you to the group chat they did it in.'

'Go on then.' He read the contents under his breath. 'Yeah, they harassed you, but it's not my place to intervene.'

'They've also sent me viruses. If word got out, you'd be shut down.'

'I seriously hope that isn't a threat.'

'Not saying I'll leak it, just stating a fact.'

A weary sigh escaped his lips. 'Listen I can believe that Rufus would send you a virus. He's done this sort of thing before.'

'But he's too valuable to lose right?'

'Yes.'

'What about me? I helped you a lot. Don't I deserve a chance?'

'You haven't proved those messages are fake.'

'About that...' *Don't fuck this up.* 'My writing and sentence structure aren't like those messages.'

'Agreed, but I don't see where you're going with this.'

'It's easy to fake these things. Can your supposed leak tell you where I sent the messages, and in what context?'

'They said you deleted them.'

'Most servers have a bot that logs all messages, deleted or not.'

'What if you sent them in a dm?'

'Then they took the quickest screenshot ever.'

'You might have deleted them after being exposed.'

'Wouldn't that make me look guilty? I'd prove them real if I did that. Also, why didn't they send them to you first? Aren't you the project lead? Leonidas and Barry surely wouldn't be the first to get such compromising information.'

'Get to the point.'

'Right, OK. So basically, Leonidas and Barry received the messages and rather than coming to you first thing, they forced me to leave the podcast.'

'And?'

'If you let them show the messages to the public, wouldn't that be a bit hit to the project's reputation? Why did they try going that route?'

'Well... don't say anything. But that's why I didn't let Barry take your place. He's too impulsive.'

'There you go, he framed me to take my place.'

'That's a big accusation. Choose your words carefully.'

'Barry always wanted to be community manager. I have screenshots from last year with him talking about it,' I began. 'He's a skilled editor, so it's not a stretch to say he could forge a Discord message. Give me some time to prove it, let me back in your server again.'

'Innocent until proven guilty? OK, I'll give you a month or so.'

'Will you unban me?'

'Yes, but if I find out you're lying, that's it.'

'Fair enough.'

He ended the call and unbanned me. Exhausted and not wanting to risk frustrating him, I didn't send any further messages. He'd given me an unspecified amount of time, and tricking my enemies into admitting the truth wouldn't be easy. Barry had long-since blocked me, so it had to be Rufus or Leonidas.

Looking back over old messages, I noted multiple weaknesses. Leonidas was a troubled twenty-something with an ever-worsening relationship with his family. But Rufus proved more than willing to engage. He had a history of conflict and a more aggressive personality, and would engage me the moment I joined Cole's server. So I waited and decided to do some research on my opponent.

In previous messages he'd told me and others that he lived in a rough part of Florida with "bad internet", and his mother had "caught cancer" from his father. Cancer isn't contagious, and Rufus never showed any signs of having a bad internet connection. Moreover, he spoke with an accent that seemed to hail from the northern United States. I couldn't prove he was lying about his situation, at least not right away. With Google as my ally, I began an investigation into his real-life situation. A Twitter account led me to a TikTok profile, belonging to someone who sounded like Rufus, acted similarly, and looked just how Leonidas had described him. I matched up the background of his videos to Chautauqua County, New York. And after gaining more information, I found his Instagram account. Neither of his parents had cancer, and he didn't live in Florida. His family basked in glamorous pools, upmarket fashions. Privately tutored in computer science and in a good school, he already had a prominent university placement lined up for him.

Spoiled brat. It didn't seem fair. He had a seemingly perfect life and nothing to lose by tormenting me. In addition to victory at tribunal, I wanted all loose ends tied up online. However difficult, I needed to defeat him or else I'd never achieve closure and a new life in Oakwood School.

I chose a Sunday when Leonidas was away. Without him, Rufus would have a harder time in battle. This risked my parents being exposed to our conversation, but if I waited longer, I ran the risk of going over Cole's time limit. The battle plans were simple, manipulate him into a confession over voice chat and record it. I spent the morning rehearsing, talking to my reflection as if it were Rufus. When the crucial hour came, bones rattled, flesh crawled, veins choked with fear in both ice and fire.

«Why is Max here?» Rufus challenged, roughly five seconds into me re-joining Cole's server. His private message to me, the first salvo. «Why are you back? Do you not understand what fuck off means?»

Before I could say anything else, he began a voice call. I turned on my recording software. *Here we go, just breathe.* Foodstuffs crushed under his molars. That "rush of cold upset" seized my body. He wasn't speaking, so I made the first move.

'Cole let me back in. Can we work things out?'

317

'If you want this to go away, you're gonna give me your account token.'

'Why do you want to get inside my account?'

'Because I'm aware you said shit behind my back.'

'You mean like how you called me a racial slur.'

'What? I never fucking... Who told you that?'

Fuck, played that one too soon. 'Uh... I don't know, he was on an alt.'

'You mean you know, you just don't wanna tell me.'

'I-I'm sorry, don't feel comfortable.'

'I don't care if you trashed me.' I closed my eyes. All that remained was his voice. 'You could say like, man, I hope Rufus fucking kills himself.' *I wish you would.* 'Like you wanna kill my family with a Katana. Is it some really graphic shit? If I can talk to the person who raped me, I can handle your stuff.'

'Someone raped you?' I blurted.

'Yeah, uh, when I was eleven. That's why I got trust issues, yeah.'

'Max, dinner,' mum called.

'Give me a second. Don't come in my room, you won't like the music.'

'Alright, don't let it go cold.'

Rufus roared with cruel laughter. 'Dude, is my voice music to you?'

'Well...'

'Ha, is that Mamma Max?'

'Yes, she's my mother. What is this, an interrogation?'

'It's not a fucking interrogation,' he scoffed. 'I'm asking you a favour. Just one thing and I'll let you go. Give me your Discord token or share screens.'

'I told you, I don't feel comfortable doing that.'

'Listen, I've been through more shit than you'd think a 17-year-old can handle. I bet you've never been in any physical brawls.'

'Out of honesty, you're just making me more un-comfortable.'

'Uncomfortable? Have you been ever been raped?'

'No, but—'

'Your shit about autism is pussy shit compared to what I've been through. Stop being selfish, it's your fault you're here.'

Don't go mad at him. 'You're right, I chose to start this conversation. But my dinner's downstairs, so you'll have to wait a bit.'

'Alright, you better not run off like a little pussy.'

I never want to feel like this again. Rufus had me, I couldn't find an opening. *How can fear hurt so much?* Never had things seemed more hopeless, even on Galactic Conquest I had people to help in battle. Now I was alone, and perhaps fear was the demon I was fighting, not Rufus.

Don't think of him. Think of what's gonna happen when you win this war. Oakwood is waiting. Rufus stood in the way of the new life I so craved, and I'd fought too hard to give up now. After eating, my train of thought returned, and a plan fell into place. *Got raped as a kid, did he? Yeah, like he lives in Florida and his parents have cancer.*

Back into the arena, emotionally bruised but ready for round two.

'I'm back, start the call.' Recording software on, I took a deep breath. Losing the war was an unthinkable catastrophe, so I focused on the most positive outcome. A new life.

'This is such petty shit and I don't care anymore. Give me your token, share your screen with me or fuck off. I wanna see what you said about me,' he demanded.

'Why don't you give me yours? Both of us should be transparent.'

'Why would I do that? I didn't say anything about you.'

'You called me a racial slur.'

'No, I... Again, who the fuck told you that?'

'Barry, he showed me screenshots from your group chat.'

'Son of a bitch. Alright, yeah, I said it. But you got him bullied with that crap video.'

'You used that slur before I made the video about him. You're lucky I'm not of that ethnicity.'

'What, are you calling me a racist, bruh? Is that what you called me behind my back?'

'I didn't call you a racist, all I said was that you're not a nice person. And that's only because I don't know you very well, so I'm basing my opinion off our interactions together.'

'I'm a nice person, I just don't like assholes trying to ruin our project.'

'Why not try changing my opinion about you then? Tell me about yourself, you went through some rough shit, right?'

'Yeah, I've been through worse shit than most people.' *Yeah, right, your dad owns a house three times the size of mine, twat.* 'Hell, you're just annoying me at this point.'

'You got raped, right? Are you strong and able to talk about it?'

'Yeah, of course.'

'I'm listening.'

'Well uh, it was on the bus, when I was coming home from school. This dude, he... uh... jumped out and did it. Pulled my pants down.'

'In broad daylight? Nobody intervened? I can't believe that happened to you, dude, I'm so sorry.'

'Yeah nobody did jack shit. It's not safe in Florida.'

'You don't sound like a southerner. Did your parents move there?'

'Uh, yeah, they had to because of cancer.'

'It sounds like you care about them, shame they both caught it.'

'Yes, it was.'

'Was? So, they've managed to pay for their treatment? Will you move back to your home state of New York anytime soon? You're a big fan of the Yankees Baseball team so I'm sure you want to go back and support them.'

'Yep, I have a Twitter about—wait how do you know where I live?'

'Florida right?'

'No, you've been stalking me. Did you think you could scare me, asshole? Because I can crush you in a few words.'

'Prove it.'

'We did it, OK? We're the ones who fucked up your little community manager gig. But no one is ever gonna believe you.' *Bingo, it actually fucking worked!* 'So you know what?'

'What?'

'Fuck you and fuck your family. Barry deserved to be community manager. Now fuck off and kill yourself, cunt.'

With that, he disconnected. *I got it all on recording. It worked.* Monday afternoon, October 22nd, Cole listened to the recording and agreed that I was innocent. However, I didn't get my former job back, and despite their behaviour he allowed Leonidas and Rufus to continue work on the project. So to ruin Rufus's day a bit, I played my trump card and reported him to Discord. Months earlier, before the incident, he'd admitted to doxing a community member. This is against the Discord terms of service, so I got his primary account banned. After that, I never saw him again. Maybe Cole kept him behind the scenes, not wanting to risk the project's reputation.

Two down, two to go. Leonidas was still at large continuing his cyber-bullying campaign against me, and the local authority still was awaiting me at tribunal.

Chapter 25: Still in the Trenches

Four months of total war had taken its toll on my mental health, and on my grandmother's birthday, I needed to leave the celebrations because of a practically skull-destroying migraine. Battle after battle, there didn't seem to be an end in sight. However, recent events had turned the tide, and almost all our expert reports were ready.

'Did you buy the exam voucher?' I asked.

'Yeah, but you're gonna book first, right?' Caleb replied.

'Yep, sorting out access arrangements is a different process. So I'll come back to you with a date soon. Hopefully, we can take the exam together.'

'Why have both of you come back from Costa Coffee?' Charlotte demanded. Rosaline stood at her side, exchanging short bursts of eye contact with Caleb.

'Rosaline said we could go.'

'I said you can go, we're not against that. But Caleb only comes in on Tuesdays. You can have a coffee with anyone, but you must use him for CompTIA.'

'We were taking a break. Besides it's smart futures day, there aren't any actual lessons.'

'It's a waste of our resources to send Caleb,' Charlotte said sharply. 'And you know you get the best deal out of anyone in Portum. And that's incredibly good for you.'

Ah, you're still holding a grudge. 'It is but—'

'We at Crown Heights School cannot offer you any more than we are now,' she stated.

'We only took a half an hour break. We're going back to work in a second.'

'Make sure you use Caleb well, because you might very well end up working with me instead.'

I made mental notes of everything she said. When left alone, I emailed my parents, so that they could pass on events to Edward, our solicitor. I disliked conceiving of Charlotte as an obstacle, but the situation at Portum continued to deteriorate for me. Resilience waned; I extended the word count of my history essays with invisible text and avoided going to lessons.

Though I did enjoy spending time with Jayden and Ludwig, who was a new TA, the atmosphere had grown greyer and more depressing, as if I were a ghost, unable to connect with my surroundings, because Portum had changed so much. In the "old days", I'd tried to avoid conflict with other students, mainly because I rather liked my head and wanted to keep it intact. But that was about to change, as Nathan, a newly joined year eleven, had other ideas. He was the strong, athletic type, taller than two of me put together. He took

pleasure in provoking Jayden, smiling whenever he got a reaction. I mostly saw him at lunchtime. In the kitchen, he'd
incite things with the more vulnerable year sevens.

I disapproved and wondered why Rosaline always
defended his actions. The way I saw it, if Nathan instigated
conflict then Jayden had full right to swear at him.

***

'Is that KFC? Can I have some?' Nathan prodded,
reaching into the box before I could protest.

Rosaline threw her hand in the way. 'Nathan, stop,
he hasn't had anything to eat all day.'

Heart racing, I dragged my lunch out of his reach.

He stepped back, grinning. 'I'm joking, I'm joking.' *So this is why everyone hates you. Another asshole in
my life, splendid.*

***

'Rosaline's in there with Nathan. I'll knock,'
Caleb said.

Give him another chance. People have done worse.
Rosaline gave the thumbs up, and we entered.

'How tall is he?' Nathan enquired, jabbing a finger
in my direction.

'He has a name, it's Max' Rosaline interjected.

'Five foot five,' I said.

He stood up, towering over Caleb and me. 'I'm
taller than him.'

'OK, great, we've established that. Now let's crack on with our English, Rosaline said brightly. 'You know Max is a master of *Animal Farm*.'

'Wait how old is he?'

'I'm sixteen.'

'He's my age and he's shorter than me,' he laughed. 'Why are you so short?'

Why are you so retarded? 'Well, Audie Murphy was my height, it didn't stop him. I guess it's just genetics.' Silently we took a chair and left.

'You handled that well,' said Caleb.

'Only because you were there,' I muttered, still shaken.

***

We were closing towards our exam date, November 27th. There were other certifications I could take afterwards to advance my potential career in IT, but everything was too uncertain for that. And Leonidas being active didn't help the situation. He'd swear at me in public servers, then delete his message, retreating when my supporters called him out.

Did I want to try recovering my position as community manager? Was it worth the immense resources? I'd achieved the main goal of the online theatre, proving my innocence. But I still lacked closure, and Leonidas still threatened me. He continued to send viruses, often saying, «I know where you live, lol.»

If Rufus returned, I'd report him for ban evasion. And though Barry piped up from time to time, he didn't pose a challenge. Things were reaching their climax, and the last week of November would prove one of the war's most crucial. I had my CompTIA exam on the Tuesday, Leonidas was getting more and more aggressive online, and the local authority was sending its expert witnesses into Portum on consecutive days. Someone had certainly done their homework, as these were the same professionals who'd assessed me in White Mountain School. I didn't believe it was a coincidence they'd been chosen this time, too. Though I didn't mind answering their questions, Portum was the selected battleground, and people were bound to be caught in the crossfire.

The week opened with a battle against Leonidas, a day before my CompTIA exam. Angered by Sebastian's increasingly apparent support of me, Leonidas tried to scare him into surrender.

***

«Took me ten minutes. I have your last name,» Leonidas said. «Does Williams mean anything to you?»

«Are you trying to dox me?» Sebastian asked. «That's against the Discord terms of service.»

«No, just showing you how easy it is for me to find you.»

«Seriously, stop.»

«And here's your address, nice house your folks got there.»

On the internet, releasing someone's real-world address or doing anything else with their personal information (doxing) is generally considered the nuclear option. Leonidas had limited options at this point; he had failed to stop me from getting back into Cole's server, failed to infect my computer with malware, and failed with his crude messages to erode my will to fight. Through threatening Sebastian, he may have hoped to scare one or both of us. But this was a mistake, as it weakened his reputation and gave the Discord staff ample reason to ban him.

«We can get him banned for this,» I said.

«I'll report him to Discord,» Sebastian said.

«I'll type up a convincing email for you.»

If the Discord support team were fast, Leonidas's account would be deleted within the next 24 hours.

«Sent it, but Cole's probably gonna fire me for this. Not that I care, though. He lost my respect when he didn't believe you,»

«Thanks, mate. I've still got something up my sleeve for Leonidas.»

«If you want me to steal his token, I don't think he'll fall for it like Barry did.»

«No, he's got a bad relationship with his parents, and we're gonna take advantage.»

I sent Sebastian a series of screenshots. «The first ones are his Facebook page, the fourth and fifth are his mother's. And the sixth? That's the message I sent her.»

«You told her he's doing that?»

«Yep, and about how he slandered her on Reddit. Can you believe it? His own mother.»

«What if she doesn't get the message?»

«Then I'll call long distance on her landline and explain everything.»

«You got her phone number already?»

«I've had it for a while, just been waiting for the right time.»

«If we're lucky, tomorrow is gonna be the worst day of his life.» Leonidas was involved in several activities that I do not feel comfortable with disclosing in this book. We had messages in which he admits to such activities, which his parents would surely meet with disapproval. The evening before my CompTIA exam, he was banned from Discord, and by the time I had returned after earning my certification, his life had fallen into hell.

«I'm only at the point of tears,» Leonidas cried, having returned on a new account. «My parents have disowned me and I've been thrown out.» His Facebook page confirmed it, relatives unfriending him, and talking about how disappointed they were. Sebastian faced consequences, but nobody knew about my own involvement.

With Barry being badly bullied in real life, Rufus out of sight, and Leonidas disowned by his own family, the online front had had a clear victor, me. The last optional objective was deciding if I wanted to try becoming community manager again, albeit I'd have to persuade Cole for that to happen.

«We're too good for them,» said Sebastian. «Come on, leave with me.»

«I haven't decided if I want to leave yet, Seb. I'll speak to you soon.»

The local authority sent in their professionals. The speech and language therapist ran the same tests she'd done with me ten years before in primary school. And the educational psychologist couldn't deny the findings of her counterpart on our side. Neither of them got to see me in class, as my history teacher wasn't at work that day.

'He's petrified outside of Portum,' Rosaline stated.

'But he was so articulate with me,' the educational psychologist said, perplexed. It had been an eventful week with multiple victories. We had a date for my tribunal now, too – March 7th, 2019. An end to the terrible conflict was in sight, and though drained I had to keep pushing.

Chapter 26: Penance?

«Hurting people is what you do best,» Draxx14 said witheringly.

«And that's why we'll never respect or forgive you,» Invicta11 added.

Fuzzy images melted into pitch-black darkness.

'Bus is outside, get dressed,' dad called.

A laborious morning routine ran on with almost comical haste, as if in fast-forward. But by the time I got downstairs, the bus had already left.

'Bastards,' dad fumed. 'I'll be late for work now.'

'There's a history exam today,' I admitted. 'If we go now, I can still make it.'

Hands over his forehead, he exhaled a frustrated breath. 'Why didn't you tell me?'

'There's a lot going on, sorry.'

The transport team didn't answer our calls or provide an explanation. So, I wrote an email.

14.12.18

Dear Sir,

I'm writing to you regarding the use of your transport service. In recent months I've been late for the bus. Today this resulted in me being left behind without warning. I apologise and understand it isn't reasonable to keep the driver, escort and other passengers waiting. However, I ask you to take my complex needs into consideration. Because of a lack of naturally produced melatonin, I struggle to sleep. I'm also stifled by a body that has, from birth, struggled to muster sufficient strength. In the morning, I remedy this by rocking on the floor, which stimulates key muscles so that they work properly during the day.

I set my alarm for six-forty, a whole hour before the bus arrives. Plenty of time, right? Often, it's a struggle to remain awake and get out of bed, as I'm waiting on my body to work. Because the bus is usually ten minutes away, I need to skip much of the typical morning routine and settle for the bare minimum.

Dressed, teeth cleaned, hair brushed, school bag on. Whilst I'm struggling to do it, the bus is outside, and they have to leave after five minutes. Today, this caused tremendous stress. The school transport arrived much earlier than my designated pick-up time and left without warning.

Though my issues have been explained by both my family and the school, I think there is a sense that I'm late on purpose. Today I had a history exam. If not for the accommodation of

Portum staff, I'd have missed it. Why would I be purposefully late? I'd just be creating more stress for myself.

All I ask is that you consider my personal situation and warn us when the bus needs to leave. For all my life, I've fought battles I never asked for. Anything you can do to ease some pressure will be of tremendous help.

Yours sincerely,

Max Toper

At first, the transport team didn't believe I had written the email, but after a few exchanges they agreed to tell us when the bus needed to leave. I explained the tribunal and other things to the escort and the driver, who were understanding.

***

'Look I'm natty,' Nathan called, playing on a scooter board that was far too small for him.

Christine shook her head. 'You're very silly.'

I refused to take my eyes off him, tracking even the slightest of movements. *I'm sure it's fine, just focus on your lunch.* Tired, and eating late after an exam, I didn't want to go hungry because of my anxiety surrounding him.

The phone in the office rang. 'Nathan, give me a minute, love.'

Once she had left, Nathan launched himself upward, kicking the scooter board out of the way. It smashed against the wall, discarded by its unsuitable pilot. He gave me a juvenile smile, closing in on my personal space. 'Baby Max.'

I clenched my hand into a shaky fist.

'Maxine, why are you ignoring me?' *Because you're a cunt.* For a while, he stared blankly. Most Portum students usually reacted to him. A whirling plastic blade prodded the back of my head. I stood up at full height, pushing away the miniature fan Nathan was using against me.

'I'm joking, I'm joking,' he laughed.

'Sorry about that, Nathan,' Christine called.

'I was looking after Max.'

'Right, that's very good of you.'

They both left, but I'd lost my appetite. Into the bin went my lunch. I'd allowed fear to defeat me.

'Christine, Nathan tried provoking me earlier.'

She grabbed a pen and a sheet of paper. 'I'm sorry sweetheart, I was on the phone.'

'It's not you who should apologise, it's his fault.'

'Don't worry, I'll tell his mum about it.'

'Nathan is sixteen, what's she going to do, spank him?'

'He listens to her.'

'So, he lacks basic common sense then? Right got it.'

'Well, we're trying to teach him. And you can help.'

'What if I'd been more volatile and something had happened?'

'A lot of our more volatile students tolerate him.'

'Tolerate him? For how long? I'm telling you, someone is gonna get hurt, badly hurt.'

'He's a smart and funny guy, he just doesn't have any concept of social interaction.'

Smart and funny guy? Is she mental?

'He has issues, but he'll mature just like you have.'

'Every other student at Portum has autism,' I scoffed.

'Some of you need more help than—'

'Say I threw that monitor out the window, and it smashed someone on the head. Would having autism still be an excuse?'

She pinched her nose, not giving me an answer.

'Never mind, forget it, I'm going to the bus.'

Jayden was the only other person I spoke to who held a dislike of Nathan. I confided in him.

***

'Why the fuck do good people leave and get replaced with twats like Nathan?' he complained.

'Exactly, Lucas would have dealt with it. Christine just called him a smart and funny guy.'

'Seriously? Is she mental?'

'That's exactly what I thought.'

'This twat needs to get the hell out of Portum.'

'I wish. Hopefully, he'll leave and become someone else's problem.'

'Yeah, hopefully.'

Jayden had often denounced Nathan. I tried to keep out of it, not wanting another conflict. But Nathan quickly developed obsessions with people, and despite my neutrality I wasn't exempt.

'Baby Max, why are you ignoring me?' Nathan shouted.

Not this asshole again.

'Nathan, leave him alone,' Ludwig requested. 'Go on Instagram or something.'

'But he's ignoring me.'

'That's his choice, eat your lunch.'

'Thanks,' I whispered. 'Can't even put my plate in the dishwasher without him starting something.'

'You'll have to put up with it, I'm afraid. We can't do anything. Charlotte would go mad.'

'Is she the reason he gets away with it?'

'Nah, it's not just him. Charlotte doesn't even let us raise our voices around you guys.'

I wanted to eat my lunch without Nathan disturbing people, especially me, and if I had to speak to Charlotte to get anywhere, I'd do it. Once everyone else had left Portum, I confronted her in the office.

'Are you gonna do anything about Nathan?'

She spun around in her chair. 'I'm sorry, is he bothering you again?'

'Yes, and other people. Are you going to do something? Or do I need to raise a student complaint?'

337

'In the past you've tried using knives to hurt others. Which is why I've hidden the sharp ones in that drawer.'

I pulled it open, discovering several knives and a hammer.

'I told you that because I trust you. Hopefully, you've matured since then.'

She's shifting the blame onto me. 'Why does my behaviour two years ago mean anything here?'

'I'm just saying that like you, Nathan will mature. He's been out of school for a long time. We were aware of that when we brought him in.'

'Did you know he'd harass students and laugh in the faces of your staff members?'

'Well, he has been harassed by students in mainstream.'

'It's called karma, Charlotte. There's always a bigger bully.' Her nostrils flared, pupils dilating. 'Kind to each other in Portum? Guess some people are exempt.'

'I know you don't want to be here, Max!' she observed bitterly. 'We don't have the resources, you know that. We just hope... we hope that he'll mature like you did.'

'Don't bring the tribunal into this. Now either you'll do something about Nathan or I will.'

'You'll do what? If it's something unkind, then it's my duty of care to protect him. '

'Trust me, the things I can do and have considered doing aren't kind.'

'Then I hope you're mature enough to control yourself. Now, would you like to continue this discussion downstairs?'

'Down to the bus? Sure, I've kept them waiting long enough.'

***

I reflected on the conversation, listening to "Blue on Black" by Five Finger Death Punch, with the world passing by as we drove. Charlotte talked about the Portum staff planning to discuss Nathan. But given her sudden explosive shift to the tribunal, it was clear the issues surrounding him were just more fuel to the fire.

She had a stressful job running Portum, and here was an opportunity to exploit it.

'Jayden, I got an idea.'

'About Nathan?'

'Yes, we're going to make surveys about him, ask people their opinions about him.'

'And when everyone says they hate him, he'll get thrown out.'

'Possibly, but I need you to distribute the surveys.'

I set our target as questioning ten students. For simplicity's sake we kept it to one question, "How do you feel about Nathan?" Below that, we gave them the option to write down any additional thoughts. The results weren't in Nathan's favour, but my plan wasn't about turning students against him. Rather, I used the Nathan issue as a springboard to convince Jayden to do other surveys. I couldn't prevent people from realising my involvement, but they'd be hard-pressed to work out the ulterior motive behind it all.

The next two surveys were crucial; one exposed Portum's relationship with the mainstream school, and the other exposed problems like a lack of resources. I'd deliver the results of the latter to Charlotte a day before the tribunal. Everyone knew Portum lacked resources, but nobody knew the full extent except her. If I could manipulate her into talking about it and record what she said, I'd be able to make an exposé that I would then put anonymously into the public domain. I believed the resulting stress would lead her into an explosive admission that Portum couldn't meet my needs, thus destroying the Local Authority's case at the forthcoming tribunal.

The other surveys played a different role. The first one had made Nathan a bigger issue and a greater source of pressure for Charlotte. And the delivery of the first two would ease her into a routine, thus making it more likely when the time came that she would reveal what I wanted. A bold plan, but did I have the right to attempt to manipulate her on such a grand scale? Had the war blinded my sense of morality? Was I proving Draxx14 right, that I couldn't control my emotions or ego?

I'd left Galactic Conquest in such a hurry and desperately wanted closure from past grievances. I made another Discord account to reconnect with the Paladins, hoping a Christmas reunion would help me to move on.

In the meantime, I reconnected with Bradford943. «Hey, mate, been a while.»

«It's been ages. Did you beat Barry and those other bastards you told me about?»

«I did, one of them got disowned because of me. I proved I'm innocent, but I'm not even sure I wanna stay there now.»

«Bah, if they're willing to target you in real life, they deserved it. That's when it becomes too personal.»

«I guess, but things have gotten shitty with the tribunal and all. I want to escape a bit, so I've made another Discord account for Galactic Conquest. I was wondering if we could do a Paladins reunion or something.»

«Yeah, everyone will be happy to see you again.»

Many people joined our gathering, but most people didn't play the game anymore, and those who did wanted me to revive the Paladins. I found it tempting. The older days online and at Portum seemed like simpler times, when it didn't feel as though the universe was trying to consume me. But childhood had had its time, and though the tribunal would decide everything, the choices leading to adulthood were still my own. A lot had happened over the last year and a half, and throughout the Christmas holidays, I had time to reflect. There were a lot of inner grievances to confront, and many questions to answer.

***

«Tbh, guys, a lot of what Draxx14 said got to me,» I admitted.

«Draxx14 was a moron,» Bradford943 said. Everyone present agreed with him.

«Maybe, but I wasn't a good leader myself. I manipulated people and often allowed my ego to get in the way.»

«Are you kidding?» said IMaginkI, challenging my self-depiction. «You were a good leader. You inspired others, treated us fairly, led us and stuck by us. You prioritised making the game fun over other bullshit. That's why I respect you.»

«Aye, same. XMA, you're one of the six people who have my respect, and the only leader I'm dead loyal to,» another former paladin added.

It was true. Every fond moment in the Paladins had been my doing as much as theirs. Yes, I hadn't always made the best decisions, but wasn't the fact that people enjoyed the Paladins worth cherishing by itself?

«See, I told you people appreciate you. And if it's closure you want, I've got a way for you to get it.»

«I won't speak to Draxx, it's too much.»

«Would you speak to one of his former officers? I can invite him to the server.»

«Sure.»

Bradford943 invited him in, and we started talking.

«I don't hold a grudge against you and your men. It was your leaders who ordered you to attack us,» I said.

«Thanks, I can see why you didn't like Sir Draxx. By the way, not a lot of us favoured Invicta and Diablous,» The officer confided.

«Really, didn't you all respect them.»

«No they treated us all like shit, which is why Major279 took over when we merged with the Shadow Imperium. When they came back I couldn't do anything to stop it.»

«Yeah, I understand, I'm sorry to hear that. We in the Paladins just wanted to go our own way because Draxx14 had changed the Shadow Imperium so drastically.»

«Nobody ever told us that, which is why we only saw it from Sir Draxx's point of view. He said you wouldn't merge with us, therefore we didn't see a way to negotiate.»

«I mean, even if you told him that, he wouldn't listen. We all thought you were traitors. At the time, if Sir Draxx had told us any different, we'd have thought he'd gone crazy.»

«About Draxx... you said he disappeared. What happened to The Shadow Imperium when he did?»

«The whole Shadow Imperium fell into chaos after you guys beat us and hacked Sir Draxx. Invicta and Diablous tried a revival, but it didn't last long. Most of us haven't seen them in more than a year.»

«I'm sorry about what I did. Hacking was going too far.»

«Nah, you guys gave us the best fights ever and won fairly. Besides, even I think Sir Draxx went too far with what he said to you.»

«I never realised you all felt that way.»

«You couldn't of, if I even tried speaking to you, I'd of been called a traitor. But a few of us respected you guys, we just couldn't say anything.»

Bradford943 suggested we sign a treaty, because technically the war had never ended. It wasn't formal, but it served as an acknowledgement that both sides had moved on and forgiven each other. And once we got to know the former Shadow Imperium members, we realised that we had a lot in common.

For me the experience brought some closure, though it didn't dissipate my wider feelings. Was I an irredeemable monster? Were manipulation and hurting others my only talents? Like Jayden and the other students who helped hand him out the surveys: was I selfish in using them for my own ends? Asleep all day and awake all night, everything had shifted into a state of disorder.

***

'Have to be honest, there's a lot I haven't told you,' Bradford943 admitted. We were in a voice call together, having spent hours playing games and listening to music.

'Back when you rebelled against Jessica, Draxx actually sent me to destroy the Paladins.'

'Wait, he wanted me out of the picture even back then?' I asked.

'Yep, he was always like that. But you earned my respect, and it was worth following you.'

'Thanks. So why didn't you tell me about Draxx back when it all began?'

'It's a long story, people said a lot behind your back, and I didn't want it to upset you.'

'Yeah, I suppose it's better you didn't.'

'Still upset about what Draxx said?'

'Kind of.'

'It wasn't you, he shat on everyone. It's why you never saw the Shadow Imperium with any allies.'

'I still shouldn't have ordered his account to be hacked.'

'Beating yourself up won't change what happened.'

'I know.'

'The world enjoys shitting on us, and you can't expect to be perfect all the time.'

'I've hurt people though, and I'm not sure if I deserve to win this tribunal. That's if I have a chance of winning at all.'

'Everyone's hurt people, mate, but if anyone deserves to go to that school and have a fresh start, it's you.'

'Do you really think I'll win?'

'Yes, and it's your job to prove me right.'

'Then I'll start now. I've waited too long to change and become a better person.'

Chapter 27: An Approaching Storm

New Year's Day 2019. After showering and brushing my teeth for the first time in days, I decided I wanted to make pancakes. Unfortunately, we didn't have the ingredients and the only shop open was a one-mile trek through an unforgiving winter-cold. The sensible thing would be to make something else. Or to wait for mum and dad.

Instead, with no sleep, I stepped outside for the first time in a week. Vigorous wind clattered in my ears, demanding submission. I sang "Red Cold River" by Breaking Benjamin under an icy breath. When I limped through the door, plagued by a rheumy cough and carrying two bags of breakfast foods, dad thought a burglar had entered the house.

My legs ached for days afterward, but it was a return to form, proof of determination, and a valuable resource in war. Back at arms, I logged into my main Discord account, ready to close the online theatre. Over the past week, I had stepped away, and in that time I could see that Cole had sent multiple messages.

«Max, the project's been hit with a cease and desist, I need a statement from you. Respond to me, please,» he begged.

I ignored him for a few days, to give him a taste of his own medicine, so to speak. When I'd been framed and was at my lowest, Cole hadn't helped me. Why did I owe him anything? In fact, whilst ignoring him I went out to eat with my grandparents, no internet drama in sight. Did I need to be a community manager, respected and followed by everyone? Ever since leaving Galactic Conquest, I'd achieved non-virtual things and had experienced other sources of happiness. With maturity came a wider and wider world, and if I believed that Portum didn't have a place in my future, couldn't I also give up the need for power on the internet?

Assisting Cole and returning to his side would have been a giant step backwards. However, leaving him and the community in peril wasn't good for my conscience, so I compromised with myself. To bring about closure, I'd write a statement to these "lawyers" and then leave my internet empire to rot. I gave myself a week to "close up shop", saying goodbye to followers and giving them a chance to play in-game with me. A lot of them had stuck by me throughout the last few months, and though they'd never learn what had happened behind the scenes, I felt the need to pay tribute to their loyalty.

A cathartic release followed as I deleted all accounts related to Cole's project and its community. Cole asked me to stay, telling me that the lawyers were blown away by what

I'd said. But I didn't stop to say goodbye to him, in fact, I'm not so sure he was telling the truth about there being any lawyers at all.

After months of brutal stalemate, things ended quickly and in the best way possible, with a resolution that allowed me to move forward. And though the tribunal and my placement in Oakwood was still uncertain, life online had never been easier. I just had one Discord account for communicating with Jayden and other pupils at Portum, and another for staying in touch with my fellow Paladins.

Freed from digital bondage, I could commit all my resources to preparing for the tribunal. Hopefully, I would win and finish my Portum years on a high note. When school started again, I tried to wake up earlier and make myself breakfast in the mornings.

I wanted to see the escort gobsmacked, but she'd already left and been replaced with someone else. Lessons didn't become any easier to attend without protest, I didn't understand the point of committing to something I might not finish, and it was hard to change that mindset.

Unsurprisingly, Nathan didn't understand that Jayden and I wanted to be left alone, even if I explained it to him. There didn't seem to be a way to end the issue, so I decided it was best to avoid him. But although my strategy reduced encounters between us, it wouldn't work as a permanent solution. Jayden and I ended up eating our lunch in private, away from the kitchen. Rosaline argued that he would lose interest if we talked to him in a "friendly way", but we didn't see him as "redeemable" or safe to be around.

I predicted escalations between him and other students, and such predictions inevitably came true. Violence erupted on multiple occasions, causing me to spend even more time in a vegetative like state inside the Turing Room.

No matter what I did, the cracks continued to grow bigger. My ability to endure was faltering after months of gruelling warfare. And with nothing to be done until March 7th, the initial burst of effort in my fight with the local authority fell into a stalemate that was even more tiring. This lasted until they launched a new offensive, sending us their evidence. Portum was an undefendable position for them. All our reports favoured a more suitable setting, and theirs couldn't offer much of a rebuttal. Mix that with my family's emotional ties to Charlotte, one of their witnesses, and you get a nervous local authority. With just under two months to go before the hearing, they moved the goalposts, citing Harbour View School as their chosen placement for me.

Two years prior, we had visited and rejected Harbour View. It was too similar to Portum, too far from my house, and thus unfeasible for me to reach by 8.30 in the morning on account of my acknowledged difficulties. When I visited, I found it too overcrowded, a tiny complex with over fifty people. I saw myself seeking shelter in their garden shed if I was ever sent there.

This, along with our judgment that their resources simply couldn't meet my needs, was why we dismissed it. Fair enough, right? Well, actually no it wasn't. Our solicitor told us that the distance, location, size, and amount of pupils weren't an argument, even if they tied into both my sensory needs and my ability to attend school there. In this war, buzzwords were what mattered most. If Harbour View offered "life skills" and "therapies", reading the fine print or inquiring how they would be delivered was secondary. You could summarise it all as a checklist, with no further reading or questions needing to be asked. If our side wanted to win, we would need to ask those questions and to put them well.

On the surface, this may seem like a simple change, but it gave the local authority a lot of bargaining power. In a SEN tribunal, the words of your witnesses usually carry the most weight, and none of ours had seen Harbour View, nor was there time to send them in. You see, time was a major factor; we didn't have the resources available to the local authority. And most families can't fight a case for long, if at all.

They also knew that every day I spent at Portum was a day less in Oakwood. So, if the unthinkable happened and I won, I'd have less time to take advantage of Oakwood, which meant they wouldn't have to pay as much. But the best outcome for them would be if I never stepped inside the school at all. So they brought in the heavy artillery, in form of an experienced barrister.

***

'It's all scare tactics,' I said. 'They want to intimidate us. Look, Charlotte's report isn't even true.'

'What do you mean not true?' mum asked.

'He can work in pairs with other pupils in class and give his opinion,' I read. 'Literally, all our evidence says otherwise, and so do I.'

'Charlotte isn't involved in the case anymore though.'

'That's not my point. She's claiming that Portum will magically get resources if I just regain my motivation. Her report is well written, but it falls apart because we've done our research. We'll have to do the same for Harbour View.'

'Yes, but we have so little time.'

'Don't let them intimidate you, that's what they want. Dad thinks we're gonna win, I think we're gonna win, so no matter what, we have to see this through.'

Was Charlotte intentionally speaking untruths? Or had she made a mistake amidst the pressure? I wanted to give her the benefit of the doubt, yet I couldn't help but feel she had malicious intent. With the introduction of Harbour View School, my plan to use her underlying emotions to sabotage the local authority's case was void. However, I felt that if Portum's problems were openly disclosed, someone would "have to fix them". So the surveys would go ahead as planned, but for a different purpose. With parents starting to question Portum's resources and its ability to prepare their children for life, it was the perfect time to execute my plan.

Two last battles awaited. One would change Portum's future, another would change mine. To prepare for the former, I researched everything I could find on Harbour View, down to even the smallest details found in pictures. What perplexed me most was how Mia, the head of their provision, who had met me for a mere half an hour two years ago, believed I'd flourish at her school. This alone didn't mean we could disprove her statement without visiting Harbour View for ourselves.

Our other witnesses were all booked, and unable to attend at such short notice. Which left only Maya, the deputy head of Oakwood, to join us on our visit. There was just one problem. The local authority blocked her attendance. They didn't believe her to be a "suitably qualified professional". Our solicitor intervened, but the local authority remained belligerent. If we wanted any of our witnesses to see Harbour View, he would need to get a court order from the tribunal. However, given his heavy caseload, this would take time that we didn't have. This gave the local authority an advantage of which they were well aware, as my words and those of my parents carried little weight. If we wanted to argue against Harbour View, one of our witnesses needed to see it.

***

353

On the day of our visit, Mia greeted us with a firm handshake and unwavering eye contact. My parents asked the important questions whilst I remained silent, scrutinising every detail of the provision. It was a small rectangular complex, located outside the mainstream school, with tightly packed structures including a garden shed taking up most of the space. Mia cited Portum as her inspiration, but I hadn't embarked on this tribunal simply to continue with the same weary educational structure. I'd done five years at Portum, so choosing a very similar placement miles away from my house would be a giant step backwards. In Harbour View School, I saw a future of regression.

I'd arrive late each morning, groggy, and full of angst, dropped against my will into a confined space with over fifty people to contend with. At this stage in my life, I wanted progression, not regression into the depths of sensory and emotional overload. Leaving Portum for Harbour View was like coming out of an oven into a furnace.

'What about OT and your other therapies?' mum asked.

'We have universal support, once every half term,' Mia replied. 'Max, all our students love it here, and I'm sure you will too.'

I've been here five minutes; how can you possibly know that? 'Um, OK.'

'Do you have a question for me?'

354

'How do your students cope in mainstream?'

'Most of our students attend lessons here. But the ones in mainstream love their classes, I think that's why they're so successful.' *She's good with words. I'll give her that.*

'What subjects are you interested in, Max? We offer a lot here.'

'Recently I passed a CompTIA certification exam, so computing I guess.'

'Outside of mainstream we offer our own IT programs. Oh, and our students help the teachers with their computer problems. Everything here is open to you.'

'Can you accommodate CompTIA certifications?'

'I don't know what those are, but I'll look into it for you.'

Whatever I say, she'll say they can offer it in some capacity. 'You won't need to, most people self-study for them. Wherever I end up, I can do it.'

'Well, we'd be thrilled to have you here. But if you want Oakwood, you need to speak up at the tribunal, because you're the best advocate for yourself.'

'Thanks, I guess.'

We were on opposing sides. But did she want to battle us? As head of her provision, advocating for my placement, there was an obligation. But I knew that if she was a committed opponent, she wouldn't have said that.

***

«It's a joke, the BTECs are primary-school level,» I said.

«You're not arguing about the courses though,» Bradford943 pointed out. «Any school can give you that. Like you said, it's about catching up with the other stuff.»

«Problem is, she'll just say she offers life skills, the therapies, and the tribunal will take her word for it.»

«That's why you have a solicitor, mate.»

«They have a barrister.»

«Our enemies always had the advantage, but the Paladins still never lost a war.»

«This is different, they'll ask me questions and trip me up.»

«Yeah, they'll try that, but like that woman said, you know yourself best.»

«What if I sort of – I don't know – talked about why Harbour View wouldn't work in great detail?»

«Sounds like a good plan. I can help you practise over voice chat.»

«Works for me, but they could make up something about me being overdramatic.»

«That's fear talking. If you make a great speech about all the shit you've put up with, its gonna look terrible if they just call you overdramatic.»

«Let's just hope I'll be ready.»

Chapter 28: The Last Battle

Nathan's corpse rested lifelessly on the floor, his face locked in horror. Charlotte stared at me with a sharp frown, unfazed by the Katana I wielded. She didn't try to stop the blade slashing through her torso. A darkness engulfed all else before melting into my bedroom. It was a Thursday, one week before the tribunal, and six days before Charlotte would receive the final survey.

After eight months of warfare, I'd fallen into a state of constant tiredness, unable to leave my bed. With the ultimate confrontation approaching, and my ability to make it to school on time gradually fading, I thought it best to stay home on some days. This way I could catch up on sleep, Portum staff wouldn't be as stretched, and the bus didn't need to wait for me.

Though everything rested on the outcome of the tribunal, fear hadn't yet taken hold of me. At this point, I just wanted an end to the terrible conflict. Most SEN tribunal cases are built on reports full of buzzwords, and how much money the local authority is willing to part with. It's very rare for a judge to meet the child they are going to decide for, so whatever I said would have a big impact on the battle. In fact, I was counting it.

To build confidence, I'd been practising with Bradford943. Though I only had days to prepare, it was the last few weeks that moved in fast-forward. The struggle had involved gruelling months in the trenches, waiting for reports, waiting for our appeal to be lodged, waiting for the opportune moment to act against my enemies online. Now, instead of waiting months or weeks, it was days. The local authority's speech and language therapist went on maternity leave, so they had to pull in another one. After four years of attendance, I'd been discharged from my feeding clinic. And the tribunal granted us a court order, so that Maya could now visit Harbour View with my parents on March 4th, three days before the tribunal. And what a day it was!

Ronnie, a TA, took Jayden and me down to get our lunch on the high road. Every time we left the school, staff signed out at reception. Today, the receptionist was none other than a biscuit-chomping Mr. Haddaway.

'Oh, crap, not this prick again,' Jayden huffed.

'OK, why are you upset with him this time?' Ronnie asked.

'We'll find out soon,' I said.

'Well, I'm sure he won't be a problem. Give me a moment to sign us out.'

Mr. Haddaway glanced up from his computer. 'Where are you taking them?'

'To get their lunch.'

'You'll need two members of staff, safeguarding.'

'Yes, because Ronnie is going to stab us and dump our bodies in the River Thames,' I whispered.

Jayden covered his mouth, concealing a giggle.

'I'll be back in a second, boys,' Ronnie said. He returned to Portum to find a second staff member to "escort us".

'What an asshole!' Jayden mouthed.

'We've never needed two staff. I swear he just makes up this safeguarding crap to piss the world off.'

'I hope our surveys get him fired.'

'We'll have Rosaline and Ronnie fill them out after lunch. Then we'll go to Charlotte two days from now.'

The two-staff rule suffocated much of Portum's flexibility. If, for example, a student wanted to let off steam in the local park, there would rarely be enough staff on site to accommodate it. Unlike mainstream students in the upper years, we weren't allowed to leave school alone during lunchbreak. Portum had to abide by the policies of the mainstream school, which limited the ways the provision could help me and other students. This was a reason for my decision to leave.

***

'Two staff?' That's ridiculous,' Rosaline griped.

'Alfie Robinson wouldn't have allowed it,' I said.

'We all miss him, he's the reason we're here.'

'I remember little about him, just that he was friendly.'

'What year were you in when he died?' Ronnie asked.

'Year seven, too young and too scared to appreciate him.'

'You'd have gotten along.'

'Too late now, but at least Portum is still alive and part of his legacy.'

'Yes,' said Rosaline. 'He would be proud. I'll tell his daughter we were talking about her wonderful father.'

'Max, the bus is here,' Jayden announced.

'I'll see you both tomorrow.'

'Wait, when is your tribunal?'

'Three days from now. Why?'

'Is Charlotte coming?'

'She isn't a witness, did the council not tell her?'

'They didn't, but thank God she isn't.'

'What do you mean?'

'She wanted to be there.'

'Oh, I thought they would have told her.'

For a week, we hadn't had an escort on the bus. There was no need for one, the children were few and quiet in their conversations. We all liked and trusted Clyde, our driver. Head pressed against the window, I listened to music, "Knights Of Cydonia" by Muse, the same song I'd played when the Paladins first formed against Jessica14 all those years ago.

Mr. Haddaway inspected the other bus, Christine meekly following behind.

'Clyde, it might be a good idea to leave,' I suggested.

'Why, who is he?' he asked.

'A bad person,' Jayden replied. 'Ah, shit, too late now, the bastard's seen us.'

Mr. Haddaway knocked on the window. 'Do you have an escort?'

'No,' Jayden answered.

'Come with me.'

'What about the kids?'

'They can wait. Now come out, please.'

He led Clyde out of hearing distance and gestured him inside the school.

'OK, something's going on,' I concluded. 'He's obviously not going in for a friendly chat.'

'What do we do?' Jayden asked.

'Get your phone out and start recording. The time is ten minutes past three, make note of that, because I have a feeling we'll be here a while.'

Clyde and Mr. Haddaway had gone inside. We recorded everything in bursts, making a note of the time and how no adult came to collect or check on us. Problem was, our bus wasn't really a bus anymore, as funding and the small number of pupils had convinced the council to replace it with a cab.

The year seven in the seats in front of us couldn't work the sliding door, and neither Jayden nor I could climb over and open it. In the seat next to Jayden's, another year seven had collapsed in the front. We couldn't reach her either.

'It's now ten minutes past four,' I said. 'Nobody has checked on us, we're trapped in here.'

'Guys, stop recording, he's coming,' one boy announced.

'Jayden, make it look like you're texting your mum,' I directed. Without hesitation, he did so, fooling Mr. Haddaway when he opened the door.

The opening chords to "Knights of Cydonia" rang in my head.

'You need to tell us what's going on,' I demanded. 'Now.'

'You're going back to Portum.'

'Why have you left us unattended on the bus for an hour? Lisa's collapsed in the front seat.'

'Oh, I was wondering why she wasn't coming out. Can one of you fetch her?'

'One of us already is.'

'Good.'

'Are you going to apologise?'

'For what?'

'Leaving us here without an explanation.'

362

'All you need to know is that we're getting two members of staff to drive you home on one of the school minibuses.'

'The old ones?'

'Yes, there aren't any others.'

'The doors barely open on those. Why not let Clyde take us home?'

'It's unsafe.'

'Unsafe? He's taken us home in all weathers since the beginning of term, there's nobody I'd trust to drive the bus right now more than him. Have you told our parents what's happening? They're going to be worried sick.'

'That's not my responsibility.'

'Then what is your responsibility here?'

'I can't tell you that. Come on, let's go.'

'Before I go anywhere, I'd like to know who's responsible for leaving vulnerable children unattended in a tiny cab for an hour.'

'You're right.'

'Exactly, and I'm not even finished talking. Two members of staff, who have no idea where we live, are being tasked with taking us home. Do you not see the issue here?'

'Like I said, you're right, let's go to Portum.'

'So you agree this is a pointless exercise, and that it would be better to let Clyde take us home.'

'Yes, but I have a job to do and part of it is following school policy.'

'There's policy and then there's impractical policy.'

'It's still school policy, now let's get to Portum.'

He herded us upstairs, then rushed off in a hurry the moment we arrived.

'Jayden, did you get all that?' I whispered.

'Yeah.'

'Good, he's not getting away with it.'

Once two teachers finally did arrive, they led us to the minibus. Its engine put up stalwart resistance, only starting after three frustrated attempts. Sweet wrappers and putrid-smelling packets of crisps dotted the floor. It took both teachers trying from inside and out to open the main door. Our disgruntled chaperones drove around in circles, ignoring our directions until they got desperate. Despite all of us living close to the school and around the same area, it took them almost three hours to get everyone home safely. When I came in, mum and dad rushed over, their glassy-eyed gazes unable to settle on anything.

'If you're wondering why I'm home late, it's a long story,' I said. 'Mr. Haddaway's fault.'

'We were at Harbour View today with Maya,' mum lamented. 'Mia was really good, they had cameras and eve-rything. They're going to be on TV.'

'We haven't lost yet. However good she is I'm sure—'

'The council wants to settle,' dad blurted out. 'We're giving the decision to you.'

'What?'

'A settlement, it's—'

'I know what a settlement is, but what's the deal? Do I get into Oakwood?'

'Yes, and you get a proper EHCP, but we have to pay a small part of the school fees.'

'You've already spent thousands on the tribunal. I want to see it through, no matter what.'

'Don't be stubborn, Edward's advice is to take the deal. He's done thousands of these, you told us to choose him for that reason.'

'I never make sensible decisions.'

'Bollocks, you have an hour. Risk it on the 7th and we get nothing, or take the deal and you go to Oakwood. We've re-mortgaged for a reason.'

My brain was a violent whirl. The cost of peace was both a monetary and ideological sacrifice.

***

«I don't envy you with this decision,» Bradford943 reasoned in an attempt to console me. «I know it feels wrong, and that you don't like to betray your principles, but can you afford to risk losing in court?»

«It's like merging with Draxx, a deal with the devil. If I take it, those bastards win.»

«You're right, they're bastards. Think of it another way though, you've forced them to the negotiating table. It's not like they aren't making the concessions you want.»

Dad was calling me. 'Max, come here, please.'

'One second.' «I'll talk to you later, my dad's calling me.»

***

An email from the local authority, they'd sent late evidence to the tribunal less than two days before the hearing. Lengthy and mostly irrelevant SEND policies from Harbour View School, a late speech and language report. If you put all the documents together, they exceeded 100 pages.

'The judges can't read all that in time,' I fretted.

'It's tactical, Max, we'll go there on Thursday and they'll adjourn the case,' dad said. 'More months in Portum, and less time in Oakwood. Even if we win, they don't have to pay for as many terms there. It's all about the money, there's only so much they're willing to spend,' he explained.

I could barely hold on at Portum. Though it violated my principles, drawing out the conflict would hurt myself and others. 'This goes against everything I believe but... Let's just take the deal, it's for the best.'

The most destructive conflict of my life ended with a few hesitantly spoken words.

***

«I didn't get home till half past seven, and they drove past Lisa's house twice,» Jayden informed me when I spoke to him on Discord later that evening. «Are you still gonna give Charlotte those surveys on Wednesday?»

«Yes, but I won't be in school tomorrow, and I have to go somewhere Wednesday morning.»

«But we'll give Charlotte the surveys when you come in, right?»

«I'll do it the moment I come in.»

***

On Wednesday morning, we met Edward in his office. He was going to walk us through the deal and slightly adjust our proposals for my EHCP.

'I won't get that' he said, crossing out a recommendation from one of our witnesses. 'We can't push our luck.'

'Are we still going to the court tomorrow?' mum asked.

'Yes, to sign the deal. And because I think you all need closure.'

Once everything had been explained and agreed upon, I went to school for my confrontation with Charlotte. Nobody knew the full extent of the plan except me. Over half-term, with the Christmas money I had left, I purchased a used phone. Concealed in my coat pocket, it would record Charlotte's every word.

Besides the surveys and the phone, I carried a laptop. When I broke into the school's network drive, I obtained an entire folder of pictures from Portum, some taken by students when the provision was first founded. I knew

367

that showing them to Charlotte on the laptop would bring her into a more emotional and open state.

***

'That's when Ronnie took them to buy Christmas presents,' Charlotte reminisced.

'Back when safeguarding wasn't an issue,' I said.

'I had to write a lot of risk assessments for those trips.'

'What I mean is, the school used to be more flexible.'

'When Mr. Robinson was alive, yes.'

'And now?'

'At first I thought Portum wouldn't work, then I thought it could, and now I'm not so sure.'

'Why?'

'It's limited in a mainstream school. I've had to make difficult compromises to appease certain people.'

'These certain people are never in Portum. Mr. Robinson came up here a lot, why doesn't his successor?'

'All I can tell you is that we aren't the priority, and that we're lucky to still be here.' Her gaze met the floor, shoulders slumped. 'I don't have the resources to cater for everyone. That's why I said we couldn't address your autism when that educational psychologist came from the council.'

'I'm sorry all those assessments had to happen. I need you to know my decision to leave isn't personal. I have nothing against you or Portum as a whole.'

'I'm incredibly pleased you've said that. We try to do our best for everyone.'

'Portum laid the foundations for my future, I'll always look back on it fondly.'

'From the moment you arrived here, we were always impressed with how insightful and caring you are. But I think Lucas saw it the most, he's so proud of you.'

'I was terrified when I first came here, thought I'd die. If not for Lucas, I don't know what we'd have done.'

'Well, you didn't die, and I think we all feel that way about him.'

'Yes... there's something I have to ask you, for my conscience.'

'Go on.'

'In your report, you wrote things that weren't true. Like how I work in groups of mainstream peers. Why?'

'Did I? I'm sorry, the report wasn't something I wanted to write.'

'It's fine, I forgive you.'

'Good, and whatever happens at your tribunal tomorrow we'll always do our best to support you.'

***

The deal hadn't been signed yet; I didn't want to tell anyone in school that I'd be leaving this term until it was final. We spoke for an hour and I had recorded everything. Combined with the footage I had of Mr. Haddaway, it would be enough to make a video exposing the issues plaguing Portum.

Years ago, I feared Portum and Crown Heights School. Now I held the power to affect the lives of every student and staff member. But would the video help Portum or hinder it? Could I afford a coin toss? What if Charlotte got into trouble for admitting certain things and lost her job?

I wanted to help Portum, yet risking the safety of everyone there only endangered it. Whatever the odds, causing harm wasn't something I wanted to risk. So I deleted the footage and other compromising pieces of information on my computer. Though it was troubling, I had to accept that the fate of the provision wasn't up to me, and that the best way to support it was through non-illicit means.

***

'If your client is in agreement, I'd suggest you sign the document now. No need to delay,' the opposing barrister urged.

'Give us a minute, please. Thank you,' Edward replied.

'It says here it is agreed that Harbour View is able to meet my needs,' I read. 'We never agreed to that. I'd like it changed before Edward signs it on our behalf.'

The barrister checked his watch, breathing a weary sigh. 'I'll be back in a moment.'

Dissatisfied with the case's outcome, the judge asked Edward if as our solicitor, he had given us the best representation possible. The war had ended on a whimper, but spectacles weren't important. I'd fought for and won a place at Oakwood, and forced the writing of an EHCP that was truly reflective of my needs. These were privileges that few children in my position are fortunate enough to obtain.

***

'Is there something you want to say, Max?' the judge asked.

'Yes, there is.'

'My colleague and I would love to hear. Go on.'

I wanted to remember the beginning, my early years. Memories surfaced inside my head, each one containing its own world and story. One came into view, beckoning to be picked. 'When I was four years old, my parents bought me a remote-control toy car,' I began. 'The kind that whizzes around your kitchen floor. Most little boys would be delighted, but I used to hide from it behind the sofa.'

'What scared you?'

'The noise, I hated it and never understood why.' I paused, another memory beckoned to be released. 'Never understood the playground either. Other children loved it, I dreaded it.'

Unshed tears welled up in her eyes.

'I thought I wanted to be like them, but now I realise that all I've ever wanted is to live my life as me. It's been a long journey to stand here, and there's always more to be done.' I paused, making direct eye contact. 'Look, you do hundreds of these cases, but I ask you to remember who your decisions really affect. Because it's not obvious in all that paperwork.'

'Is there anything else?'

'We'd be here all day.'

'I saw what you wrote for the tribunal,' her colleague said. 'Very impressive. Have you considered writing a pamphlet or something of the sort for other young people?'

'No, although I've wanted to write a book since I was young. People have suggested it, but I don't know if I'll ever do it.'

'Well, if you do, I'll be one of the first to read it.'

'Thank you, miss.'

Settlement signed, everything wrapped up. At my request, Ronnie and Rosaline jumped through the safeguarding hoops and took both me and Jayden out for lunch on the second-to-last day. Though many Portum students hadn't interacted with me in any significant way, they all said goodbye, even Nathan.

One thought crossed my mind as I made the infamous journey from the playground into Portum for the last time. In year seven, terrified, I'd counted up the amount of times I'd need to do it in the years ahead of me then. And now it was over. Before too long, I'd left in the car with my grandparents, watching as the school faded into the distance.

Epilogue

I don't know how to write this section. Seriously, I'm telling myself that it's simple, just "write what you feel". But feelings change, and by extension so will how I view the first sixteen years of my life. All the memories, the story, it's all there now on these pages. Before I talk about me, and how I am in this moment, I'd like to thank all the people who helped me get here .

My editors, typesetter, cover artist, friends in the Paladins and "Cole's community" who helped construct the "online sections" you've read. And it isn't just them who got me behind this keyboard, able to express myself. Mum, dad, thank you for being the best parents in the world. Grandma Sheila, I'm sorry we lost baba before he could read this and see how far I've come. But he's with me, here in my heart, and I know that you always will be, too.

There's a lot of people outside my immediate family who I'm proud to call my friends. I used to think I'd be forever abnormal, that I didn't have an identity or place in the world. You helped me see otherwise. I have my low moments, for sure, but on the whole I appreciate myself for who I am a lot more than I did.

There's an elephant in the room with this book, autism. I didn't write a whole lot about the condition, even though being diagnosed with it is what led me here. Thing is, I genuinely don't view myself as an "autistic" or as part of some wider neurodiversity clan where our disabilities are superpowers. I view myself as Max Toper, and I don't want to be anyone or anything else.

So what happened after I left Portum and what's next? My worst fears for Portum came true for a brief moment when the Local Authority tried withdrawing funds from Portum and places like it. Luckily, they didn't succeed, and I'd like to believe that amongst other voices who cried out, I played a role in reversing their decision. I got into a chain of emails with one of the borough's MPs, proving to them that a lot of these vital provisions are starved of resources.

I'm doing tremendously well at Oakwood and am set to leave next July. It isn't a magic school that instantly "fixes everything". Yes, I've used their resources, and yes, I've met a lot of wonderful people there, too. However, growth came from me as the individual, and I owe it to everyone around me to keep growing as a person.

Life isn't fair, and I know more challenges await me in the future. But finishing this book is a great achievement for me, and I hope you've enjoyed reading it just as much as I've enjoyed writing it.